When the School Horse Was King

When the School Horse Was King

A Tribute to Faithful Friends and Companions

John C. Charyk

Western Producer Prairie Books
Saskatoon, Saskatchewan

Copyright ©1988 by John C. Charyk
Western Producer Prairie Books
Saskatoon, Saskatchewan

Cover and interior design by John Luckhurst/GDL
Cover painting by Don Frache

Printed and bound in Canada

The publisher acknowledges the support received for this publication from the Canada Council.

Western Producer Prairie Books is a unique publishing venture located in the middle of western Canada and owned by a group of prairie farmers who are members of Saskatchewan Wheat Pool. From the first book in 1954, a reprint of a serial originally carried in the weekly newspaper *The Western Producer*, to the book before you now, the tradition of providing enjoyable and informative reading for all Canadians is continued.

Canadian Cataloguing in Publication Data
Charyk, John C., 1908–

When the school horse was king

Includes index.
ISBN 0–88833–271–8

1. Rural schools - Canada - History. 2. Rural
children - Canada - Education - History. 3. Horses -
Social aspects - Canada - History. I. Title.

LB1568.C2C42 1988   372.971   C88–098090–7

Contents

*For my sisters, Mary Ferenz and Helen Forrest, and brothers,
Nicholas and Joseph, and their families,*

and

*for all those pioneers across Canada who, in one way or
another, contributed their precious time and energy toward
making the one-room schools a truly proud moment in the
growth of a great Canadian nation.*

Preface

This is not an all-embracing study of transportation in early western Canadian education. Neither is its virtue entirely in its prose, or even in the comprehensive collection of historical photographs. I hope you will find here the same delight as you would in an old family diary or photo album in the attic.

Through the years 1880 to 1970, school children were kicked, stepped on, ran away with, bucked off onto hard ground, or whatever by school horses, yet they still look back at those long, cold, windy, accident-filled trips, repeating, "Those old nags saved our lives!"

In our age, monuments have been erected to honour race horses, bucking broncos, superior show horses, as well as historically famous equines. Yet no one has cast the figure of the once-common school horse that according to experienced children used to rank at the top of all species of horses. These were work horses in the fields, pack horses on the long and dusty trails, but first and foremost, they were entrusted with the safety of the children they carried to and from school in all kinds of inclement weather.

School horses did not conform to any particular breed or line of breeding. There was no standard size, shape, or colour, but there were clear-cut requirements in disposition, reliability, and understanding of their small masters. These animals could be giants like Clydesdales; range to miniature beasts of burden like Shetlands; or even manifest themselves in the so-called rough-cast Indian ponies. Despite inexperienced young drivers, the selected pony rarely permitted the buggy or cutter to strike a gatepost and upset. Youngsters learned to drive and take care of their horses by doing it; it was almost as if horses were part of the general curriculum of the rural education system.

School horses were like people: some stubborn, some humorous, some cranky, some tricky, some affectionate, some intelligent, and so on, but these singularities made each one special. All are gone and almost forgotten now; the only way to learn something about them has been to listen to the stories of the pioneers who remember their special school pony. Listening takes time—it has taken me over twenty-five years to accumulate these narratives and historical photographs.

Are you ready to enjoy this book about one aspect of educational history in Canada? Here it is!

Horsey! Horsey!

You ain't in a hurry,
You ain't in a flurry,
You ain't got a very heavy load.
So-o-o
Horsey, horsey, don't you stop,
Just let your feet go clippety-clop
Your tail go swish, and
Your wheels go round and round,
Giddy-up we're homeward bound.

Written and composed by:
Box, Cox, Butler and Roberts
Copyright 1937, by:
The Sun Music Publishing Co. Ltd.

1 | King of the Road

Horses made an outstanding contribution to the development and progress of education in rural areas of Canada and the United States. The proverbial Little White Schoolhouse disappeared almost completely when the bright yellow school bus replaced the school pony, with its open shay and its counterpart, the open sleigh, but this transportation system of the past logged millions and millions of miles taking school children to and from thousands of schools. Horses were as much an integral part of the education system as the pupils, teachers, books, equipment, and programme of studies.

In Canada and the United States, horses tilled millions of acres of land before the tractor became functional, without any battle glory—just plain hard work. Out of this group came the school horse.

Children in the early days walked to school, but an occasional few were fortunate to be able to ride or drive horses. In the "unimproved districts" where school areas could not be organized, some pupils had as far as nine miles to reach the nearest centre of education. Horses were very much a part of this way of life, and they played an important function in the history of education.

Saddles were considered an expensive item, and dangerous, so the majority of the students rode bareback, but there was no end to the variety of horse-drawn conveyances in which the children rode to school: buggies, democrats, buckboards, wagons, stoneboats, carioles, and an occasional surrey in the summer, while sleighs, cutters, jumpers, toboggans, and the persistent stoneboats took over during the winter season. Some of the units the homesteaders built to carry their children to school were ingenious, to say the least. "Necessity was the mother of invention" as far as these hardy homesteaders were concerned.

The Robinson family had a number of alternatives when it came to transportation in 1924: the old buggy, the new Model T, or the faithful school horse. As usual, the children seem to have been most interested in their friend Pinto. The family's two dogs, however, preferred the upholstered Model T.

A poster of forty years ago advertising a farm sale usually carried the information that a number of the animals offered for sale were "suitable as school ponies." This meant that they were gentle, easily managed, and had a liking for children. This was occasionally found to be false advertising. More than one buyer found, to their dismay, that their newly acquired animal would have made a better rodeo performer than school horse.

Most school horses were gentle though—they had to be! Cecil Green, who lived in High River, Alberta, starting in 1913, stated, "I can't tell you too much about using the school pony or driving a horse that brought the children back and forth from school as we walked. I remember some of the horses the neighbours' children used to bring to school, though. You could crawl between their hind legs, and the animals never used to kick or anything because they were so used to children!"

In addition to providing the children with a convenient means of getting to and from school, these horses were family pets. In most cases, a close relationship developed between a child and his equine. The child was responsible for feeding, watering, grooming, and looking after all the comforts of the horse, while in turn, Old Faithful provided recreation and transportation for his young master. Imagine caring for a nine-hundred-pound baby, and you have an idea of the job these rural children accepted. The school pony was also the equivalent of our present-day second car, for it played the role of freelancer on the farm, performing the less dramatic duties such as getting the cows, rounding up other horses, and running errands.

After all these rides, neither the children nor Old Faithful would soon forget the

These sixteen school horses made an important contribution to the education of the children of the Westbrook S.D. (Cochrane, Alberta).

3

musical rattle of the rings on the bridle, the strong smell and melodious creaking of the leather saddle, the clip-clop staccato of the horse's hooves, or the breezes whipping across the faces of both horse and rider, blended as one, as they raced to school or went after the cows in the pasture. No wonder the ballad "Old Faithful" used to be so popular.

2 | A Sense of Responsibility

Parents placed a good deal of trust in both their offspring and the school horse. Each had the potential to seriously hurt the other: the horse by losing its way in a blizzard or bucking the child off onto the hard ground; and the child by neglecting his friend or abusing him. No parent deliberately selected a horse that was too spirited for his children to handle. School horses had to be gentle, patient, and (it seems) old—the older the better! Few frisky three-year-olds were thought to be experienced enough to handle a five-year-old driver. Parents did not neglect the other party in this relationship, either. Before their children went off to school on Old Dobbin for the first time, they were taught at least the basics of riding or driving. Experience, of course, would teach the rest.

Horse and child were each dependent on the other for their safety and well-being. They needed each other, and this is the strongest foundation on which to build a friendship.

Training Horse . . . and Rider

It was never easy for a beginner to learn to harness and hitch a pony to the buggy. Every school morning found the novice standing on an upturned pail or box, adjusting the various straps on a horse which, to a third grader, must have borne a close resemblance to an elephant. But the majority of horses were understanding and stood patiently while the young and inexperienced hands fumbled at their task. The horse did its best to back between the proffered shafts of the buggy, its hind feet tapping the ground like a ballet dancer in an attempt to feel for the rigging. The boy was more of a nuisance than a help in this regard—he never held the shafts very steady, and in backing up the horse, he

Margory Story, an expert driver at the age of eight, bridled and hitched up this team with the help of her three younger brothers for the twice-daily trip to Rush Centre S.D. 2769 (Oyen, Alberta) in 1940.

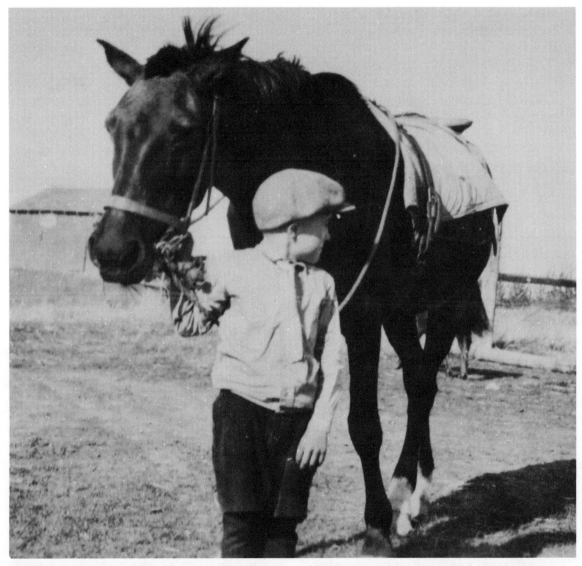

Eldon Person, decked out in a pair of knee-high pants, a tie, and cap, is all ready for a day of learning at Hudson Heights S.D. 3716 (Sibbald, Alberta). His most difficult problem of the day, though, would be how to get on Bessie's back with only a heavy blanket for a saddle and, hence, no stirrups. He ended up having to climb up on a fence to get on!

invariably mixed up his "gees" and "haws." Is it any wonder that the confused pony had to glance back several times to correct matters? After a bit more of such fiddling, buggy and horse would be ready to start for school . . . maybe! One could almost guess what the horse was thinking: "It's taking hìm a long time, but his *is* learning!"

In 1920, George Holford and his sister Dorothy rode a very beautiful, high-spirited, dapple-gray four-year-old to Mona Lea S.D. George was small for his age and so had devised a unique method of mounting his horse. He would grasp the leather ties on the side of the saddle and climb up, the tiny toes of his bare feet digging into the horse's leg. The moment he reached the horn of the saddle, he would make a wild scramble, and presto, there he was in the seat. While all this was going on, the horse would look around from time to time to see how George was making out. Sometimes those little toe nails must have been very sharp, but never once did the horse move the leg that the young lad was walking up. And yet that same horse stood on his hind legs and bucked a few times when mounted by George's father.

We children learned to ride a horse, as the expression goes, before we were knee-high to a grasshopper. At first Dad would tuck us comfortably in front of him on Nina's back; later we were allowed to sit alone, short legs dangling and hands grasping her mane, while he walked beside her holding the bridle reins. One early, frightening solo ride for me was the time Nina decided to give herself an ex-tra shake after her dust bath, propelling me toward the prairie trail. Dad rescued me in midair, lowering me back on Nina to continue my ride home.

For the most part, the students were their own drivers. However, if they were too immature to be entrusted with a horse, their mother, with a baby in her lap and probably some other preschool youngsters tagging along, took over the reins. Mothers, in those days, were their own babysitters and rarely left their offspring with anyone else.

The girls did not have to take a back seat to the boys in this matter of driving or riding horses, for they were just as capable and sometimes even better. They usually dealt more gently than the boys with horses, much in the same manner as a mother speaks a little more softly to her child and handles him more gently than does the father. Many ponies respond readily to this type of guardianship. The boys were usually best when the horse required good, strong discipline, but even the girls were forced to use this method when all else failed—as Daisy Pierce's efforts had.

In those days, schools were not so readily accessible as now, and although we were only two miles from the Red Wing School, I was supposed to go to Lousana, travelling in a horse-drawn school van, covered wagon, or sleigh, according to the time of year. These were rather different than the motor buses school children travel in now. Dad wouldn't agree to this, so I stayed home until he pur-

Seeing their small children in charge of a big horse must have made their mothers nervous, but the children had to get to school somehow! This dedicated school horse, Pat, took Winnie Hayter and Bill Dreheer to Oxbow S.D. (Oxbow, Saskatchewan) in 1920.

chased a pony, named Queenie, which I then tried to ride to Bellgrove S.D. 2390.

This was a very trying experience for a frightened city girl who had never had anything to do with a horse. Queenie didn't like to be hurried, so every time I used my switch on her, she kicked viciously, making me even more scared—if possible. This went on for a few days, causing me to be late for school. Then Dad stepped in. Riding another horse and carrying a whip, he followed me; every time Queenie kicked, Dad used the weapon. A few days of this practice educated Queenie—and me!

But no matter how short of perfection their horse's manner really were, the children often pampered their school pony as though he were a champion dressage horse. Louise Jordison's mother thought her daughter's school horse believed she was really a show horse, for that was how she expected to be treated.

One year, when we were short of horses, my husband bought two unbroken colts. He spent a week trying to teach them to lead, but the filly wallowed in ignorance. A recent homesteader volunteered to attempt to break her in return for two sacks of oats. After a series of sessions in which he made her work very hard, usually with an older, reliable horse, she became grudgingly manageable.

Louise, my eight-year-old daughter, attended the James River Bridge S.D. (some thirty-three miles northwest of Olds). She was a great horse lover and, having watched the breaking of the filly, remarked that it ran just like a very awkward girl at school. So our horse became Clarabell and was classified as a pacer.

This young horse had not been broken, but Irene Garriott's daughter, Jean, had visions of a horse of her own to ride to school: "They were busy teaching her how to be ridden in a corral behind the barn. Then Jean rode her around to the house and asked to have a snapshot taken. After I gained my composure as a mother, I took this snap."

One day soon after seeding, I saw, to my horror, Louise riding Clarabell around the corral. Soon she was riding her to get the cows from the pasture. By fall, Louise had claimed Clarabell as her school pony. She rode her mostly bareback. Once, when riding in the bush, a branch shoved her off the animal's back, injuring her leg rather badly. Clarabell returned, at full gallop, to the house, so we knew something was wrong.

Every granary and gate had to be nailed shut or Clarabell would find a way to open them with her teeth. On weekends, if she found a gate open, she would hike down to the school and spend her day there. She would stand for hours being combed and brushed, then lie down on her side with her feet stretched out so my daughter could manicure her hoofs and wax them with floor wax.

Fred Jorgenson had an interesting experience with a school horse called Flicka.

Young Fred, after completing a teacher's course in the Calgary Normal School, accepted a position in the Wenger Heights S.D. 3007 (New Brigden, Alberta). He boarded at home and covered the five miles to school each day on horseback. Everything went fine for a few months.

As winter progressed, such a thick mantle of snow covered the ground that only the spiny twigs of Russian thistles were visible. For some inexplicable reason, Flicka developed a practice of shying at these grotesque figures in the snow.

Fred found it difficult to retain his seat on the horse at such times, and after experienc-ing a few nasty falls, he decided to break Flicka of her bad habit. His solution was to guide her directly over the projecting thistles that lay in their path. Fred reasoned that familiarity with the offending plants would lessen the horse's fear of them. He was right! Flicka no longer jumped whenever a plant reared its ugly black head above the snow.

The young teacher was on the point of praising himself for being such a good trainer when he suddenly realized that something had gone awry with his teaching. Flicka had over-learned her lesson. Now, she voluntarily sought out the thistles, no matter where they were, just so she could trot over them. Flicka's whimsical practice added another half a mile to the distance Fred already travelled to and from school.

Mistreated and Seldom Praised

The horse has a natural ability to acclimatize to a wide variety of weather conditions, but it has some basic needs, such as food and shelter, which must be provided by its owner. The horse's coat begins to grow thicker in fall. This thicker covering is the animal's first line

Food for livestock became so scarce in 1936 that Russian thistle was cut and hauled to the Helmsdale S.D. 4165 (Oyen, Alberta) for the horses to eat at noon. This group of youngsters is bringing in a load of Russian thistle in a stoneboat.

of defence against the icy blasts of winter. The hair not only gets denser but also tends to stand up, adding to its insulating qualities, and the horse's metabolism becomes more efficient in drawing energy from its body fat store. Nonetheless, it's difficult to put weight on a horse during winter, as much of the food taken in each day is used to keep warm. Shelter is required primarily for protection from the cold, wind, and snow. Basic shelter can be a simple as a stand, hills, shrubs, or trees. High winds reduce the insulating properties of its hair covering, and when the coat

gets wet, its protective properties are further reduced, increasing heat loss from the horse.

Most children treated their school pony well, but some simply slid off his back after he had taken them safely home and left him to fend for himself. On cold, windy days this was a hard-hearted thing to do, but often the children's parents were to blame for such neglect. Either they did not teach their children to look after the animal or they gave their youngsters an old, worn-out horse and a thick cudgel. What child liked to be left behind while the others, on younger mounts, travelled so much faster? No wonder poor old Dobbin was whacked so many times and received so little pity or care upon reaching the barn. Yet these same old ponies proved faithful to the very end, in spite of the treatment they received.

Maxine (Smith) Reeder's school horse, Strip, ran for quite a number of years—with some encouragement.

You know, from the time we (sometimes two, but more often three of us) got loaded up at home, we took turns kicking him and never stopped for three miles. Just as we passed the school, the end-riders slid off, while the front rider directed him into the barn with the other horses, dropped the reins, and dashed into the school. We never heard of such practices as loosening the cinches, taking off the bridle, or other such technical devices. Our horses were always well-fed at home, with a generous portion of oats twice daily, lots of hay, plus a big trough full of pure spring water.

On this particular morning, there were only two riders on Strip, my younger brother, Waldo, and myself. Since it was early spring, the ground was very slippery and wet from the heavy rains. We were loping along a fence line when Strip's feet began to slip and slide in every direction. When he finally came to rest, he had fallen away from the fence. When he stood up, his left front leg hung at a ninety degree angle to his shoulders. Needless to add, he wasn't much good after this incident.

It looks like the young owner of this mare hadn't quite gotten around to unsaddling her for the day yet. Her colt seems a bit concerned.

Dina seems a bit overburdened. However small the bodies may have been, there were still seven of them, which is asking a lot of even a patient school horse.

In the Warmley S.D. (Kiseby, Saskatchewan), the Martenson children tormented their school horse to such an extent that the riled animal became difficult to manage, particularly en route home. Their father put a stop to their actions. The Martensons owned a mule that they hitched up with a horse to carry out odd jobs about the farm. In place of the abused pony, this animal was given to the youngsters to drive to school. The boys had been in the habit of fastening a nail to the end of a stick and employing this weapon to prod the horse. They tried the same treatment on the mule, but since a mule can kick straight back, the persecutors received their just deserts every time they attempted it. The kids soon learned to leave the animal alone.

In the Monmouth S.D. 3699 (Burstall, Saskatchewan), Ella Schauer's school horse was struck on the head by a stone thrown by one of the pupils. From that day onward, the horse shied at the slightest arm movement made by any of the children. The horse also took a sudden dislike to the boys and girls, and the Schauer children experienced one runaway after another. Even the big boys became fearful of hitching the animal to the buggy.

There were no laws protecting animals from cruelty in the twenties and thirties. Betty Hantiuk now believes that her family's school pony, Old Jack, was only one of the many horses who were taken for granted, mistreated, and seldom praised for their essential role in the education of country children. At the time, though, she had little sympathy for this champion of slyness!

On our homestead, near Vegreville in east-central Alberta, we had numerous horses. My father, being an indifferent horse breeder and a loser as a horse trader, had the oddest assortment of horses in the area. One member of this freaky herd was assigned to us for doing errands and to use as a school horse. We always called him Old Jack, and although he may have been fairly young when turned over to us, he aged rapidly under our callous treatment.

Old Jack was of no recognizable breed. In fact, Dad said he was just a nag. The horse was a dirty grey with one white eye, which he rolled ominously whenever he felt overburdened. Old Jack had two gaits: his usual ambling walk, which was broken frequently by pauses to raid tempting forage along the way, and a hard, bone-jarring gallop, to which he resorted only after repeated beatings with our willow switches. The more we abused him, the trickier Old Jack grew, until he eventually became the acknowledged champion of slyness amongst school horses.

En route to school, his basic ruse was to affect lameness so that we kids, in sincere sympathy, would jump off and lead him, limping, behind us. Released in the schoolyard, he immediately forgot his disability and raced around with his horse chums. Old Jack also perfected the art of shying, and although pro-

vided with blinkers (leather pieces attached at eye-level to the bridle straps), he could spot the slightest unusual movement—or he'd invent one, and would startle so violently, we kids invariably hit the dust. The final, and most effective, of his tricks came when he had been forced into a gallop. Charging resentfully along, Old Jack would abruptly stiffen all four legs and come to such a sudden stop that anyone aboard would sail over his mean, lowered head. Fortunately, all of Old Jack's shenanigans hurt nothing more than our pride since we always rode bareback and, thus, were easily thrown free and he was sensible enough never to trample or kick us.

The Johnston children used this homemade cart to travel to Arnold S.D. (Sedgewick, Alberta). Barney pulled the cart, all four children, a cream can of water, and his own lunch: a bundle of oats.

In winter, when my brother grew old enough to drive, we hitched Old Jack to our small homemade box cutter. All five of us children squeezed in, along with our books, lunch pails, and an oat sheaf for the Ridgepark S.D. There Old Jack, hot from pulling his heavy load through unploughed snowdrifts, would be stabled alongside the other ponies in the draughty school barn. It was so cold in that shed in January that even the big boys, who liked to smoke and tell dirty stories there, did not hang about.

Needless to say, they never bothered to rub down their sweating horses; nor did they clean the barn in winter. By spring thaw, the frozen manure was piled so high behind the horses that their skinny rumps scraped on the rafters of the barn.

Usually any abuse was completely unintentional. When thoughtlessness or neglect resulted in injury to their horse, the children were shocked and full of remorse, and in the end, they learned to consider the consequences of their carelessness.

Sidney Stuber of Willow Lake S.D. (Seven

A school horse and cart all dressed up for a parade at school in Viking, Alberta. This pony is sporting a flag on his head and is pulling a cart weighed down with decorative leafy branches and flag-waving children, though they can hardly be seen for all the foilage.

Persons, Alberta) blamed himself for a tragic accident that occurred in the barn. He tied his pony with a rope that was too long and was terrified and stricken with remorse to find his much-loved pet had fallen into the manger and strangled himself.

We Doctored Her for Three Weeks

Most school ponies were given excellent care. The child of that era and his horse were no different from the boy of today and his jalopy. The keen tot of the Little White Schoolhouse days spent considerable time tinkering with or adding distinctive decorations to his mode of transportation. The pony was groomed, the buggy polished, the harness cleaned and oiled, and such knickknacks as tinted pom-poms, gaily coloured harness rings, and tuneful bells were added to give individuality and class to the running gear. Anytime the school horse suffered such casualties as saddle sores, lameness, or barbed wire cuts, he was treated like a sick child.

The Barretts—Agnes, Jimmy, and later, Georgina—lived three and a half miles from Handale, and when they started to school in the fall of 1927, they rode double on the same horse. When winter came, their dad drove them in a sleigh every morning, returning for them in the late afternoon. In spring they had a buggy and horse. The first horse was an old sorrel, Ben, who was subject to spells of colic. Once in a while, he took sick in the school barn and couldn't get up, so the children had to walk home. It was then that Dad went after him with some medicine and waited until he was well enough to get up and go home. The medicine was a mixture of ginger water and turpentine. Next day, Old Ben would be back on the buggy, ready for another trip. He was very willing but very slow. When urged to trot, his tail swung back and forth in time with his step like a metronome.

Gladys Evans, who attended Royalton S.D. (Richdale, Alberta) in the thirties, remembers using a stoneboat as an ambulance, an effort that was successful largely because of a co-operative patient.

One evening in the thirties, a stranger with about fifteen horses visited our house. He asked Dad if he could herd them into the corral for the night. Soon the horses were fed, watered, and checked, and our visitor was invited to stay overnight in the house.

In the morning, he presented Dad with a little pony, and our father, in turn, offered the animal to Wilfred and me. We named her Kitty and began to use her as a school horse. We immediately discovered that this animal knew how to travel, and before we knew it, we were at school. What a surprise!

17

All eight pupils of the Parr S.D. 2429 (Hanna, Alberta) rode to school in 1918. The two children in the front have tied a rag around their school horse's nose to keep the nose flies away.

Eventually, Kitty presented us with a colt, a large animal we called Daisy. We continued to ride her to school, but she bucked us off frequently. Then one day, Daisy became sick at school. My brother, John, and the hired man went out with the stoneboat to get her. Daisy whinnied loudly as she heard them arrive at the barn. The hired man immediately asked, "How are we going to get a sick horse on the stoneboat?" As if in reply, Daisy got up clumsily, staggered onto the stoneboat, and lay down. We had no difficulty in getting her home. When we arrived at the barn, the sick horse once again stood up and strode over to a stall at the far end of the building. We doctored her for three weeks, and gradually, she regained her health.

3 | Getting There

In the morning, the students converged on the Little White Schoolhouse from every which direction, arriving on every kind of horse—from Shetland pony to Clydesdale, from thoroughbred to mule—and in every kind of vehicle imaginable! Children were packed into carts and cutters, occasionally enjoyed the luxury of the Bennett buggy's upholstered roominess, suffered some very bumpy trips in stoneboats and toboggans, and cosied up to the heater in cabooses and vans. Sometimes the children ended up walking, trailing but never catching their unco-operative horse.

Open Shay and Open Sleigh

Space was an important factor in arranging the pupils in a transportation unit, and an effective system had to be devised. Jemina (McFadden) Webester of Teat Hills S.D. 3276 (Hughenden, Alberta) describes the way her gang rode to school.

We rode to the Teat Hills School in an old racing cart. Dorothy and I sat on the seat, hanging on to one another for dear life to keep from falling off. Jessie sat on our knees and drove Pat, the pony. Loretta sat on the floor, permitting her feet to hang out. Jessie kept a constant watch on Dorothy and I, and if she thought we were not attentive, she gave Pat a sharp slap on the rump. He'd take off like a shot! We certainly learned to hang on tight, and believe me, that schoolhouse was a sight for sore eyes!

During the winter of 1935/36, Abe, Annie, Katie, and William Braun drove to the Blumenhof S.D. 4089 (Blumenhof, Sas-

katchewan). Being the senior of the four, it was William's responsibility to hitch up the horse, Nell, and drive her to and from school, about two miles away.

We drove only in winter time when there was sufficient snow coverage on the ground to handle our stoneboat. It was a curious travelling device! The stoneboat was made of boards secured from the lumber yard in the nearby town of Blumenhof. The unit measured approximately four by six feet, with a twelve-inch frame surrounding the exterior to prevent us from falling off when driving and to keep our blankets from gliding along the side of the "boat." In addition, there was a seat built facing front which enabled two of us to sit down; the other two sat on the floor behind the bench. As our stoneboat had no tongue to hold it back in case it slid, the outfit often struck the horse's hooves.

There was plenty of room for Thelma and Doris Hughes in this homemade rig on their daily trips to the Iddesleigh S.D. (Brooks, Alberta) in 1934.

The stoneboat was a curious vehicle. These children travelled to Cravath Corners S.D. *(Hussar, Alberta) on a stoneboat, enduring the rough ride twice a day.*

One particular afternoon, on the return trip from school, our horse was frightened by a couple of other groups of children also travelling in our direction, and he bolted. The incident occurred about a quarter of a mile from home. Our stoneboat upset, strewing children, blankets, lunch kits (syrup pails), and books along the roadside. When our parents returned home that evening, they gathered up the paraphernalia lying about, puzzling over the mysterious cause of the accident.

J. Hazel Paton wrote an interesting account of a school horse in "The Green Cart," published in the Oxbow *Herald*.

In my childhood, there were no yellow buses to stop at our gate to take me to school in town, almost three miles away. My dad made me a pony cart and painted it dark green. I was very proud of it, for many of the carts that jigged their way to school each day were not so carefully made. It was meant for a pony to haul, but it often had a larger horse

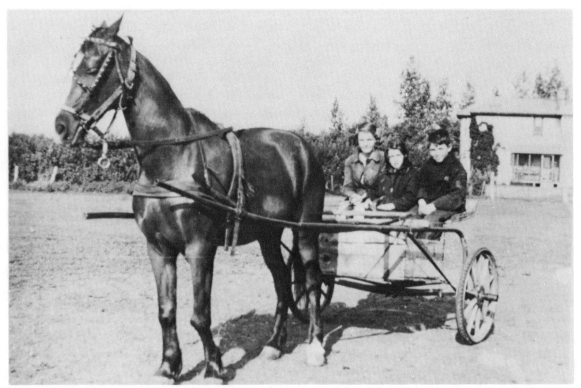

This light, bouncy cart was built by the father of these three youngsters for their trips to Bede S.D. (Melita, Manitoba) from the metal-rimmed wooden wheels, axle, and springs of an old Model T Ford, the iron piping from an old gate, some boards, and pieces of scrap iron. It was unpainted, but who could afford such luxuries as paint during the Depression?

hitched to it, and then it jiggled twice as much! The full cans of cream that I frequently took to the creamery in town would splash and splatter out onto my books and lunch kit.

During the fall and winter, if snow was absent from our rather poor roads, it was a cold, bumpy trip that I took each day, huddled on the seat of that little green cart. A big, black cowhide robe saved me from turning to solid ice. Feed had to be taken for my pony, usually an oat sheaf or some hay stuffed in a bran sack. My horse wasn't too co-operative at times and would swerve to the side, causing the cart wheel to catch on a fence post somewhere along the way. As a result, I'd have a broken whiffletree or a spokeless wheel and a very irate dad!

We did have a four-wheeled buggy that my dad used in those hard, car-less times, but eventually the wheels all found their way to the pony cart. There was no money available for new ones. A cart with one wheel larger than the other isn't exactly comfortable to ride in. I rode my horse some of the time, but as homework and bookloads increased, the cart eventually was used entirely. My dad didn't like riding in it, so my mom and I used it the most, between school trips and quick toddles for repairs for the farm machinery. Having no telephone meant bouncy trips, too, if we needed a veterinarian for the livestock, though most of those calls seemed to come during the winter when the sleigh would probably be in use.

The little green cart played a part in my limited social life too. I remember travelling five miles in it one snowless winter on Christmas Day to my uncle's place. We were a bit crowded, the three of us, but Christmas was one time my dad would not argue about the mode of transportation, just as long as he got to visit his relatives. My mom and I would sometimes drive to a neighbour's place to call, though my mother felt it was not fair to leave my dad at home so those trips were few and far between. I went myself many times, often on horseback, but the cart got to know the various roads, too. I didn't mind the jiggling in the cart, even if my dad did!

Boyfriends came on the scene, and the cart transported us quite well. One Royal Airforce boy thought it was a real lark to drive with the pony and trap, as they called a cart. By then, our family was using a car again, but I wasn't yet old enough to drive, and anyway, horse and cart travel was slower and more romantic! Modern kids would split a seam if they had

to suffer such indignities.

A dream of mine when I was a girl was to drive a race horse on a trotting sulky. My green cart didn't quite fill the bill, but my brown pony could really make its wheels spin. A friend thought he had a fast horse, but I soon left him and his horse behind when I headed my pony and cart down our country road!

At harvest time, afternoon lunch was often taken to the field with the pony and cart. These trips were up to the mark for me if I was home from school on time, for there were often some young harvesters on the threshing outfit. They would come to get their lunches and coffee from the containers in the cart, and I would be the centre of attention, something to my liking, for there were no brothers in my home.

One day, our dog and a neighbour's dog, both being very protective of their owner's respective stook racks, got into a ferocious fight under the cart. Away went my pony, the cart riding right over both dogs and almost upsetting several men eating their lunches. The dogs appeared none the worse for their accident, and I got my pony under control very quickly. I surely got laughed at, though I didn't think it was as funny then as I do now.

The cart was driven by human power at times, too. Our drinking-water well was almost a quarter of a mile from the house, so sometimes after a hot afternoon of haying, someone (me) would be dispatched to the well, pushing the green cart with a five-gallon cream can on board! I found this trip not to my liking, but the pony was not always readily available if she happened to have a foal with

The automobile becomes a sleigh when mounted on runners! In 1933, at the height of the Depression, Tom and Dick, a team of school horses, took Amanda, Adeline, and Alice Scneider to the Albeck S.D. (Cypress Hills, Alberta) in this memorable vehicle.

her. Luckily, the cart was lightweight, for there was a slight incline between the well and the house, and that cart sometimes seemed to weigh a ton! But how lucky we were to have that good water in those dry years.

The old green cart sits now under the trees in our yard, slowly returning to the earth which grew the trees it was made from so long ago. I wish now it had been stored inside for

protection against the elements. It withstood runaways, heavy loads, and broken wheels, but rain, hail, sun, and frost have taken the greatest toll.

To those who spent a good part of their younger lives jiggling along in a pony cart, I hope this will bring back some memories.

Magdalene Bernal, who attended country schools in Saskatchewan from 1937 until 1946, rode to school in all kinds of horse-drawn vehicles but never in a car.

What fond memories I have of those contented, happy, carefree days! Most of the time we walked the one mile to school, but there were occasions when the horse was our only mode of transportation. We had no car!

Sometimes it would be raining very hard after school, and how glad I was to see Mom with black Nellie hitched up to a one-horse buggy waiting outside for me. A few times, when the thermometer dipped to twenty or thirty below zero in Fahrenheit, Dad hitched up a horse and took us in an open sleigh. True, we had warm bricks wrapped up to keep our feet warm and an old buffalo robe and blanket tucked around us. Later, in the forties, the open sleigh was replaced by the luxurious closed caboose that had a small heater in it. Our first caboose, however, had no heater and an open window in front so you could pay attention to the horses. Caboose number two had both a heater and windows, while caboose number three, in addition, was erected on springs, so it operated smoothly, unlike the bumpy ride given in the others.

Six children rode in this caboose to Sunrise S.D. 2709 (Killam, Alberta) in 1930. Such a load required a team to pull it, but this *match, a big old workhorse and a Shetland pony, is an unlikely combination.*

It also had a rather streamlined appearance about it, with a curved roof—not pointed like a house.

One morning a big snow storm materialized, leaving the road across the pasture badly drifted. Suddenly, the caboose toppled over on its side, causing us to tumble out the door. The horses remained very calm and stood still. It was fortunate for us that the stove lid had remained closed, otherwise we might have been burned. That actually happened to a girl in the district, who was badly burned by hot coals scattered from the stove when her caboose upset.

Once in a while, the boys persuaded Dad to let them drive the stoneboat to school. This amounted to a large platform with no sides erected on runners. In fact, it was a real feat of balance to maintain your equilibrium while trying to stand still. Occasionally, my brother, who held the reins, would suddenly spur the horses to go faster. We'd all tumble off, try to catch up, and finally jump on again. It was the acme of exercise and excitement!

Laura (Berg) Woods's brothers, Glen, Howard, and Norman and sister, Hazel, drove a couple of work horses named Dolly and

Dan to the Pathfinder S.D. 3690 (Vermilion, Alberta) in 1936/37.

Mr. Berg built a caboose to convey his children to school. The front had a couple of small glass windows so the road and horses could be seen from inside yet the driver and passengers were protected from the variations of the weather. Because of an apparently defective digestive system, Dan always had loose bowels and was certain to plaster the glass window on his side somewhere along the way. The usual routine followed was this: As soon as the Pathfinder School was in sight, Glen would stop the team, while Howard got out and cleaned the window with handfuls of

hay or straw. This action saved the Bergs from being teased and ridiculed about their horse.

Before consolidation of schools began, each individual family looked after their own means of conveyance to and from school. With the coming of consolidation, however, transportation became part of the school's burden and was a factor that precipitated arguments and problems for many years.

The residents of the district were given the opportunity to "drive van," with the driver supplying the horses and the school supplying the vans. These horse-drawn vans were covered vehicles with canvas sides—on bobsleds in winter and on light wagon wheels in

Students at the Consolidated School in Lomond, Alberta, in 1919 were transported   *in horse-drawn school vans.*

summer. The vans were equipped with foot-warmers in which charcoal was burned. In later years, special winter vans were constructed with small heaters to keep them warm. Actually, school vans were more like a covered wagon than anything else. Winter vans were just like a box on runners and, being top-heavy, were easily upset. Sometimes when there were heavy snow drifts, the van-full of kids had to get out and help the driver tip the van back onto its runners.

It was a long day! Children never saw daylight at home except on Saturdays, Sundays, and holidays.

In some years, van driving was let-out on tender. However, during the Depression, anyone who so desired was given an opportunity to drive van to pay their taxes. Such an arrangement created a number of arguments. Some residents wouldn't accept a turn; others wanted their shift at certain times of the year; and some, when they did drive, employed short-cuts which evoked their neighbours' wrath when children were not picked up according to the statutory rules. Many people remember van routes and van driving as central issues at the annual meetings, providing the impetus for yelling matches, arguments, and sometimes actual physical scuffles, now recalled as one of the entertainment highlights of the year.

From the minutes of the Delburne Consolidated S.D. board meeting on February 9, 1918, we learn that three van-driving contracts were let; two of these were for five dollars per day each, and the other was for five dollars and fifty cents per day. The round-trip

The Bennett buggy in 1940. Major, the school horse, never needed repairs and could be counted on to get Alfred and Ethel Vallieres to Grantham S.D. (Vauxhaul, Alberta) on time.

mileage of these routes would be approximately sixteeen miles, not considering any sloughs, hills, or bush that the van would have to detour around. The upkeep of the vans was a recurrent problem, as witnessed by numerous entries instructing van drivers to bring in the vans for repair. In some cases, this too created arguments and aroused the ire of the van driver concerned.

Everyone who ever lived on a farm harbours memories of good horses and bad ones, and we still laugh about the antics of some. Lois Argue lived in the southeastern part of Saskatchewan and travelled to school via horse, but she walked a million miles.

Our home was five miles from school, so between 1926 and 1937, carts or Bennett buggies were usually made for us out of old scraps of material. One cart had haymower wheels on it, so you can imagine how rough they were. The wheels were about twenty-five to twenty-eight inches in diameter, lowering the cart considerably, so everything was thrown into it, including snakes.

Old George pulled this strange contraption. He was dark brown in colour, old, worn out, and very, very, very slow. We tried everything to increase his gait, but nothing worked. Old George hung his head continually and certainly never showed enthusiasm about anything. Later on someone built me a very smart looking turn-out, painted black and white, with buggy wheels on it. Many different horses pulled it, some slow, some fast, and I imagine Old George pulled it too.

Horsepower!

There were other novel ways of getting to school. In 1915, the Mack boys, James and Ted, of Opal S.D. 3024, (Czar, Alberta) used this unique method. Since they had only one horse to ride, and he could carry only a single passenger, they employed the "ride and tie" method. One would ride a predetermined distance then tie the animal to a tree. The other would walk to where the horse stood, take his turn riding the animal, then tie it up, permitting the other lad to ride again. According to the boys, it didn't always work: "Ted would not tie, and that was one of his tricks."

A teacher in the Wolf Willow S.D. 3370 (Merid, Saskatchewan) owned an ancient buckskin nag that rejoiced in the name of Clayton. The young lady had arranged with the Winter family that in return for her room and board she would bring the cows from the pasture every evening and drive the children to and from school.

Clayton or "Clayt" as the boys and girls loved to call him, must have had quite a past! He had five brands on his yellowish hide, all of which showed up distinctly whenever he got wet. Clayt was troubled with rheumatism to the extent that whenever a damp spell came along, he was so stiff at the beginning of the trip that he could barely walk for the first half-mile. After that, he limbered up and improved with every step.

He disliked one particularly steep hill on the way to school. It was his habit to stop part way up the hill, turn, and look pleadingly at the occupants of the buggy. If all passengers took the hint and disembarked, old Clayt continued to the summit. But if anyone remained in the carriage, he absolutely refused to go on. Instead, he would set his rump into the breeching and back up. The buggy would jackknife, and Clayt would stop short. This was the last call for all aboard to jump out; if they did not, the horse would continue to back up and eventually upset the rig. Once the human cargo was evacuated from the buggy, Clayt would take off up the slope like fury, fearful lest any of his passengers attempted to board again and augment his load. Clayt was too sagacious and experienced to be outwitted by man.

According to their sister, Monica (Boulter) Smith, Fred and Ralph Boulter's school pony, Buster, may not have been so shrewd. He either never got wise to the double duty asked of him, or he really enjoyed the trip! The two boys attended Wheatland S.D. 4059 (Acadia Valley, Alberta) where, Fred, like many pupils at the time, was the school janitor. It was his responsibility to light the fire, pump the water, clean the blackboard brushes,

sweep the floor, and dust the school furniture and windowsills each morning, ready for school opening at nine o'clock. Upon his early arrival at school, Fred turned Buster loose. The animal headed straight for home, where he was caught and turned back toward the Wheatland View School with the second son, Ralph, aboard.

The Delorme family of St. Victor, Saskatchewan, must hold some kind of record for driving the same team of mules to school for the longest period of time. Their eleven children drove Jenny and Bichou for twenty-one consecutive years.

Jenny and Bichou, the two mules who served the Delorme family so faithfully for twenty-one years.

In 1937 Mr. and Mrs. Leo Delorme began sending their three oldest children to school in a homemade cart pulled by the two faithful mules, born in 1927. Leo was then eight years of age and was appointed driver by virtue of being the oldest member of the family. When this boy outgrew the local rural school and went away to attend high school, the next eldest assumed the responsibility of driving the others. This process of seniority continued on down the line until the youngest of the eleven ceased attending the school. For twenty-one years, the Delorme children travelled the three miles to school, no matter what the weather, driving the same two loyal mules, Jenny and Bichou.

At one time there were six children attending the school from the Delorme household. In order to provide some measure of comfort and safety for such a large travelling brood, the concerned parents went to the trouble of constructing a neat, snug cubicle on a Bennett buggy. The children found travelling to and from school in this new fangled contraption comfortable in all types of weather.

By the fifties, Jenny and Bichou had slowed down to such an extent that the children found it necessary to leave home a little earlier each succeeding year to reach school on time. The working days of this devoted pair of mules ended in 1958. That year, the Montague Lake S.D. was closed, and the Delorme children were conveyed to the new central school in Willow Bunch, Saskatchewan by bus. The end of an era had come.

The Road Was Our Battleground

Once the matter of riding the horse or driving the buggy was puzzled out, the real drive to school began. However difficult their lessons might be, there were times when the trip was the most challenging part of a student's day.

"I had my own pony, Tiny, as stubborn a creature as there ever was. We were three and a half miles from the Kimberley S.D., and I used to leave home at 7:30 A.M. in order to reach school in time. Every gate, every road, every intersection became an endurance contest between the two of us. We would go round and round in circles and finally, if I won, we would continue on our way to school, but if she won, we went home at a full gallop! It would take my father's full effort to get us back to school!" recalls Barbara (Wager) Wallace.

Rosie Clifton's family drove an old horse named Curly in a single buggy to the Daly Creek S.D. 1076 (Granum, Alberta).

Our cousins also came to school by horse and buggy. Curly was balky, and since our cousins knew this, they would race by us—and there we would sit. Our horse wouldn't go ahead, he'd just back up. We all had to jump out to escape getting hurt. James whipped her, Henry tried to lead her, but all she would do was move backward and upset the buggy. How our cousins enjoyed teasing us!

In addition to the sometimes impossible task of imposing their will on a horse with different ideas, youngsters faced other obstacles on the road to school, including difficult fellow passengers and their own desire not to go!

The lengthy trips Marge (Crisford) Norris and her brother Arthur made to Highland Park S.D. 2519 (Sibbald, Alberta) behind the school pony afforded plenty of time for the two to "get to know each other."

Often, after a frustrating day at school, we would spend the trip fighting. As the youngest, I often received the worst of it. I soon devised a delaying tactic: I'd grab Art's cap and throw it out. Of course, I'd have to run back to retrieve it, which either broke up the fight or gave a needed respite. By the time we arrived home, our frustrations had disappeared, and no one knew of the battles.

When we drove to school in the early thirties, the Woods children travelled the same roads. Although Art and Bob were usually the best of friends, for a few weeks they carried on a silent feud, the trail to school serving as their battle ground. We were always ahead of them in the morning, so we would stop at several piles of blow-sand along the way and Art would run over, read a message Bob had left the night before, rub it out, and hastily write his own. I was never allowed to read these messages, on the feeble excuse that someone had to hold the reins. I knew they were probably profane and unfit for my youthful eyes, so . . . . Anyway, the rift was soon forgotten and this small intrigue discontinued.

According to Russel Palziuk, commuting to and from Henley S.D. (Lafond, Alberta) when one lived three and a half miles away offered many challenges.

As among most children, fun sometimes turned into an argument, and I remember my sister, Florence, giving me a bad time one day. I felt it was time to teach her a lesson, and as the snow drifts were very high, I steered the horse right into one of them. Florence, completely encompassed in a quilt, did not realize the apple-box type cutter was upset, trapping her inside, as I walked beside the upset vehicle. The horse continued to slowly walk home, pulling this topsey-turvey cutter. After one hundred yards or so of screaming, yelling, and roaring at each other, our argument was finally settled. I was the boss! The cutter was righted and the journey continued with a suspension of hostilities.

The three Golds sisters attended Lillico S.D. 2208, some four miles north of

Craigmyle, Alberta. Gwen Golds loved school, as did her sister Dorothy—once she got there! It didn't take much to discourage her though, when going home again seemed to be another option.

One memory of riding to school in those days stands out clearly in my mind. My sister Gwen was riding in the saddle with me perched behind her. The road, that morning, was covered with sheer ice. We had gone half a mile when the animal's legs slid from under her and she fell. Gwen, realizing what was occurring, managed to jump to safety. By the time I knew what was taking place, the horse was sitting on her rump with my stubby legs straddled around her wide tail end. To a seven-year-old youngster, this beast of burden seemed as large as an elephant. We sorted ourselves out from the wreckage, and I soon made up my mind not to continue this journey to school.

"I'll bring the horse over to the fence so you can get on," suggested Gwen.

"No! No! I'm not getting on. I'm going home," was my reply.

"Look! Dad's walking down the road!" cautioned Gwen.

Sure enough, my dad had seen the commotion and was coming to check it out. It didn't take but a minute to convince my sister to bring the animal over to the fence so I could get on, and off we went to school. Dad, seeing everything was satisfactory, turned around and went home.

The wife of Dr. Allan Ronald of Winnipeg, Manitoba, describes an interesting incident concerning her husband and his school horse, Dolly. Allan was nine years of age at the time and invariably found himself "home again" instead of at his rural school near Portage la Prairie, one and a half miles away. This became such a regular occurrence that the boy was forced to tell his dad that Dolly didn't want to go to school. His senior was having none of it: "If you or Dolly return home again, you'll both be spanked!" The result was amazing! They never had trouble going to school again. This boy-horse harmony of action is truly amazing.

While both students and horses may have dragged their feet a bit on the way to school, going home was a different story. The same student who could hardly keep his eyes open at 3:15 was wide awake at 3:30; likewise, the thought of a warm barn, rest, and food put new life in his tired old horse. The same horse that gave his master a quiet and uneventful tour of the countryside in the morning took off like a demon at 3:30.

The Grassy Slope S.D. 3993 (Hanna, Alberta) had a rickety little shed in the school yard which served as a shelter for the students' horses in the winter time. After standing shivering in this flimsy shed all day, Catherine (Faupel) James's horse, Buck, was really anxious to hit the trail!

I'd saddle him, put his bridle on, and lead him to the school porch. Once I had him standing beside the porch, I'd climb on the threshold and leap into the saddle as fast as I could. The second I was on his back he'd be off and running as fast as he could go.

Sometimes, I'd land behind the saddle and would have to stay in this position all the way home! I think I was the talk of the community, as people saw this "yellow streak" flash by.

Elizabeth Kreider's horses were in a hurry to get home too, though no one described them as a yellow streak.

My brothers and I rode the same two horses almost every day while attending school in the Buena Vista S.D. (Camrose, Alberta). One of my brothers and I rode Dick, a big, lazy sorrel gelding, while my other brother rode Topsy, a little black pony. On the way to school in the morning, the horses would drag along as though ready to drop dead at any moment, but the return trip was different. They seemed to increase their speed with every step that brought them nearer home. By the time the farmyard was in sight, they would actually be trotting.

Amy (Walmsley) Biegler's parents owned a farm near Gravelbourg, Saskatchewan, but moved to Falkland, British Columbia, in 1934 when Amy was three years old. Amy never rode a horse to school, but her brother and eight sisters did. Her story illustrates the point that breeding isn't everything: one of their race horses had a very short career as a school pony because he found his rider too much of a burden in the race to get home from school.

I recall Dad having a few race horses. One of the mares, Helen, became high-spirited in the spring. Dad decided it might quiet her

The "yellow streak": Buck, a beautiful palamino, and his rider, Catherine Faupel, in 1939. The two came home from Grassy Slope S.D. 3993 (Hanna, Alberta) very quickly.

down if my brother, Eric, were to ride her to school. Well, Helen transported him to school without a hitch, but under no circumstances would she allow him to ride her home. The minute the pair were outside the school gate, Eric would go sailing off, and Helen would make a dash for home without him. Poor Eric tried everything, but every evening Helen would arrive at the barn with an empty saddle.

4 | The Frowns of Fortune

Parents were understandably worried for the safety of their children when these unfledged horsemen first started to drive or ride to school by themselves. Such anxiety persisted for as long as the daily jaunts continued, whether for one or ten years. The children, always carefree, did not realize the dangers involved in a runaway. A horse shied at a tumbling Russian thistle, a flock of startled partridges, a leaping rabbit, a darting gopher, a fluttering leaf, or anything else that scuttled out in front of the sensitive animal. The sudden, unexpected movement often hurled the riders to the ground. Then the panic-stricken equine dashed madly for home, leaving the youngsters behind. There was no sight so alarming as a riderless horse galloping down the lane or an empty buggy rumbling into the farmyard. This always presaged a mishap of some sort! Someone immediately retraced the route, gazing around anxiously for the missing kids, uncertain whether a minor upset or a very serious accident had occurred. Nosebleeds, cuts, scratches, bruises, bumps, sprains, fractures, even fatalities occurred while travelling to and from school.

Runaways

One day, the two Branton brothers were driving home from the Eaton S.D. (Craigmyle, Alberta). Everything was going along as usual, with Harold driving and Stan sitting beside him wishing that the horse would travel a little faster. Harold decided to stretch his legs a trifle and stood up for a spell. Unexpectedly, the horse gave a sudden lurch, which knocked Harold to the ground and sent the lines flying free in the air like a couple of serpents. The startled horse, Chubby, began to gallop away, with Stan in the buggy, completely helpless to stop the runaway. Several boys riding horseback followed in close pursuit. Instead of giving assistance, they merely increased the panic of the alarmed Chubby.

He galloped all the faster!

Norman Hunter, a neighbouring farmer, hearing the stampede roaring up the road, dashed out to stop the runaway horse and rescue the helpless lad. As the barbed-wire gate was closed, he elected to jump over it rather than lose precious time opening it. Mr. Hunter's courageous leap over the fence coincided perfectly with Chubby's appearance on the road outside the gate. The dumbfounded horse took to the ditch and came to an abrupt stop when the buggy wheel crashed into a telephone pole. Stan was crying! Harold was crying! Mr. Hunter was attempting to calm the nervous and frightened horse. Luckily, no one was seriously injured. And all participants, Chubby included, had learned a worthwhile lesson on how not to act on the way home from school.

A few of the older boys in the Superba S.D. 2984 (Oyen, Alberta) decided to play a joke on Harvey Johnstone, one of the pupils. He rode an ugly-looking, razor-backed pony, which may have had something to do with their choice of victim. They slipped some burrs beneath the saddle girth just before the boy started for home. Now, this particular horse had a peculiar habit of suddenly jumping sideways when his rider least expected it anyway, and with the sharp needles pricking his body at every move, the animal took to sun-fishing in a most professional manner. Harvey tried to dismount after managing to stay with the horse for some distance, but in doing so, his foot caught in the stirrup. After that episode, the boy was grounded as far as horseback riding was concerned. From then on, the poor fellow was forced to walk the three miles to school.

Not all school children involved in runaways escaped with a mere shakeup, superficial injuries, or shock. Some were maimed for life and others, killed. A fatal accident in the Potter Creek S.D. (Rimbey, Alberta) had an element of the supernatural woven into it, for it seemed to have been foretold.

As it was a cool fall day, the door of the Potter Creek School had been closed, and only one window at the back had been left open a few inches to provide ventilation. All at once, the quiet of the room was disturbed by a bird that had squeezed its way through the small opening. It circled high over the heads of the students and then, for some inexplicable reason, landed on one of the boys, Jimmy Fisher. The teacher, Thomas Randall, took a broom and attempted to chase the bird out of the room, but with little success. The bird fluttered away momentarily, then lit on the head of the same youngster a second time. Finally, two of the older boys picked up their hats and, with the teacher's assistance, guided the persistent bird out through the door, which had been opened when the pursuit began.

When Mrs. Cashie Prosser, who had come to pick up one of the students after school, was told of the incident, she said, "They shouldn't have been unkind to the bird, especially when it had to creep through such a small aperture in the window to enter the school, since it had come to bear someone's soul away. It's a warning of death!"

Later that same day, the accident occurred.

In the act of mounting a saddled horse behind another boy, Jimmy Fisher's heel accidently came in contact with the horse's flank. No one had warned Jimmy that the horse would buck if its flanks were touched. The horse bolted, after throwing the other boy clear, but Jimmy Fisher's foot was caught in the stirrup. He was dragged for nearly a mile and died two days later.

Equipment Problems

Hills always signalled danger for children riding to school in any type of horse-drawn vehicle. Now and then, the holdback snapped during the descent, and the unfettered buggy ran ahead to smack the animal in the rump. Unless he was of an extremely quiet disposition, the sudden contact and insult to his dignity alarmed the animal and impelled him to flee. As he raced ahead in an attempt to keep away from the prodding vehicle, the buggy, in turn, gained momentum as it careened crazily down the incline. Such a wild ride usually ended at the bottom of the hill with a smashed buggy and injured youngsters, though the children were fre-

This gig looks sturdy enough, but the two little girls, on their way to school near Elgin, *Manitoba, in 1909, hardly look ready to handle a runaway.*

quently able to jump to safety before the final crash.

Agnes, Jimmy, and Georgina Barrett rode to Handale School in one of two buggies, neither of which was sturdy enough to remain intact for long. Grateful though he was that his children were not seriously injured, their father found the constant repairs infuriating.

One day, while jogging along, a bolt broke under the buggy, causing the front wheels to come loose. Old Ben kept on going, dragging the wheels, but the buggy fell forward, and the three children were hurled over the dashboard onto the ground. Ben went a little farther, then realized his load was too light, and turned around to look back at his passengers on the ground. They walked home again, leading Ben this time, while their dad went back for the buggy. Their dad was heard to mutter that it kept him busy fixing one buggy while the kids were off to school wrecking the other.

Learning to Fall

Horseback riding had its potential dangers. Hazards like gopher or badger holes, icy spots, ruts, and hidden stones or roots could trip a horse and cause it to stumble. When this happened, the child could be thrown to the ground with sufficient force to result in grave injuries. Sometimes junior was not thrown free but was pinned to the ground by the weighty animal falling on him. Such accidents could be very serious.

Many parents forbade the use of saddles. They were afraid that if the horse bucked or reared backwards, the child's foot might get caught in the stirrup as he was tossed from the animal's back. The thought of a child being dragged along the ground by a runaway horse wasn't very pleasant.

This buggy doesn't look quite so sturdy—note the precarious angle of the right front wheel! No, it's not about to fall off; it's a harrow-cart wheel, an improvised replacement for the original.

The Payne boys, school bag slung over the saddle horn, on Topsy. Geoffrey may have been a touch annoyed about having to take up the rear, but Tom suffered a bit for his privileged position in the saddle.

That's what happened to the Payne brothers, Tom and Geoffrey, who rode double to Earltown S.D. 2417 (Hanna, Alberta) in 1924.

On our way to school, we stopped at a well half a mile down the road to draw water for the cattle. My older brother, Tom, who was twelve years old at the time, rode up front with me bringing up the rear on our horse, Topsy. It had been raining, so there was no need to water the cattle. The horse turned into the gate from force of habit, slipped, and unfortunately, fell on her side in the mud. I was thrown clear, but my brother, whose feet were bound by the stirrups, was caught under Topsy when she dropped to the ground.

When I finally reached him, his right foot was pointing backwards—definitely broken. This incident occurred directly across from the Sutherland residence, to which I quickly ran for help. Mrs. Sutherland dashed out and, with my brother straddled across her back, trudged back to the house. My folks were notified immediately, and he was taken to the Hanna General Hospital. Unfortunately, a week later, he was sent home after contracting the measles.

No saddle for this young man, Robert Westra, on his first day of school. He had all he could handle just hanging on to the reins and his lunch bag.

Vi Duncan now wonders how she could have given her two little girls, Gwendolyn, eight, and Marilyn, five, the responsibility of driving to Avebury S.D. 4198 alone. On this particular day, the girls were clutching a rake to clean the schoolyard with on Arbour Day in 1948.

Saddles were indeed troublesome things for children. It seems that the more equipment the child had to deal with, the more opportunity there was for an accident. Sam Clayton attended Gamble S.D. (Carbon, Alberta) from 1915 to 1924 and was quite an experienced rider—then he got careless.

May, one of the neighbour girls, drove a single buggy to school. It was always a race to see who could leave the schoolyard first when school was dismissed. Once, in my haste to be first, I neglected to tighten Dexter's cinch. As I climbed into the saddle, May was hitching her horse to the buggy. The saddle slipped and rolled to one side. Dexter started

to buck! I tried to right the saddle, but the pony bucked between the side wheels of May's buggy. I went sailing through the air, landing forcefully on the buggy seat. I scrambled out of the buggy, none the worse for wear after my tumble, tightened the cinch carefully, and rode on home.

Marguerite (Hittle) Warner, on the other hand, fell all the time on the way to school and so became quite good at it.

I was to survive dozens of tumbles on our rides home from Rearville S.D. Lewis, my brother, was pilot for our six-mile school trip, rounding up the milk cows on the way home. My job was to carry the lunch kits, water container, and book bag, and by necessity, I achieved a bit of balance as we trotted up hill

Are they safe? It looks as though there's nothing to stop this horse from running away with these two Sunnynook, Alberta, cowgirls.

41

and down over prairie trails. Arriving at the pasture gate, Lewis would bring Nina to a sudden halt and slide neatly off. I, too, came tumbling after, landing with a thud amid lunch baskets and all. However, unlike Jack and Jill of nursery rhyme fame, I didn't break my crown, and since I was never hurt (probably having learned, by necessity, to fall in a relaxed fashion), Lewis thought this hilarious fun.

These oft-repeated incidents ended rather abruptly when I struck a rock, fracturing my collar bone. My brother was most concerned, for upon reaching home, I quietly trudged upstairs and fell asleep. At supper time, our parents investigated the incident. I remember being afraid to tell them of my daily tumbles, particularly as Lewis was now very meek and repentant. Next day, we drove in our Model-T to the Cereal Municipal Hospital, where Dr. Esler examined my injured shoulder. I remember having to wear a sling for several weeks.

Daisy Pierce maintains that her training continued right along.

When Kyte S.D. 4118 was opened, I went there. My sister, Gertie, was also going to school, and she rode behind me on Queenie. Anything less than a gallop was too slow, so we rode, up hill and down, at full gait. One day while going down hill, the cinch broke.

"Whoa!" I said. Well, Queenie stopped suddenly, but the saddle, Gertie, and I didn't. We went sailing over her head onto the trail in front of her. Fortunately, we were not seriously hurt, but I had learned another lesson. Next time the cinch snapped, we didn't stop but rode it home.

5 | School Time

The rural schoolyard came dramatically to life each morning the moment the youngsters arrived. The common procedure was to drive up to the steps at the front of the school to discharge the passengers and facilitate the unloading of books, lunch pails, and possibly a cream can of water. The driver then completed his duty by parking in his favourite spot near the barn. The last jaunt was rarely made alone. Inevitably, a flock of youngsters hung on to the rear of the buggy and let their feet drag along the ground or simply ran behind. One or two of the driver's special friends clambered aboard to keep him company and pass on some supposedly confidential information. Soon the horse was unhitched and let into its assigned stall in the barn. Not all horses could get along with each other, so it required a bit of study and experimentation to discover which animals could be put together and which ought to be kept apart. The bridle was exchanged for a halter and the rope made fast to the hayrack. Just enough slack was left in the cord to provide some degree of comfort for the animal.

The conscientious student always took the trouble to make his horse comfortable before leaving for the schoolhouse. He saw to it that his horse had an ample supply of dry, clean straw in its stall, that no part of the harness was irritating the body, and that, on cold days, his four-footed friend was covered with a warm blanket.

The Barn

Once the chore of preparing the horses for the day was completed, the boys straggled into the school to cluster about the stove on cold winter mornings or in the cloakroom on mild days. Here they reviewed any local happenings. Their patter in the schoolhouse remained on a respectable level, but topics concerning girls, the teacher, philosophy of life, sex, or anything slightly off-colour were reserved for the barn, where they felt safe from any undesirable eavesdroppers.

It must be assumed that this practice of leaving the discussion of "delicate" subjects to the safe confines of the barn was initiated by the adults and emulated by the rising generation. No social visit to a farm was ever complete without someone suggesting a stroll in the direction of the barn. It might be to see a prize calf, to examine a sample of wheat, to try out a new pump, or to throw some feed to the livestock. Whatever the reason, everyone relaxed as the men and boys headed in the direction of the barn, while the women and girls were given the run of the house. Characteristically, the conversation of both groups took a sudden and dramatic turn toward life in the raw, and niceties suffered accordingly.

The barn was an integral part of the rural school complex. Sooner or later, the school board was confronted with the problem of building a stable to provide shelter for the many horses that conveyed the children to school. If the exigency occurred at the time of the school's organization, the barn's construction was made a part of the original contract; if not, the building was delayed until a definite need arose. Then, at the appropriate time, a tender for the barn was advertised, or as happened in so many community-minded districts, the school board purchased the building materials and the people of the area organized a building bee to erect the shelter.

The early settlers in the Ridgeview S.D. 489 (Blackie, Alberta) sponsored regular socials in order to obtain sufficient funds

The school barn and privy at Lanfine S.D. 2640 (Lanfine, Alberta).

with which to build a stable. They celebrated their success, most fittingly, by holding a Thanksgiving supper in the new barn before turning it over to the school ponies.

The size of the barn, its design, quality, and workmanship were purely a matter of local requirements and preferences. In some districts, it was a well-constructed shanty; in others, a mere makeshift of two or three buildings that had been neglected and had fallen into disrepair. Even the most basic structure served to keep the horses comfortable in all kinds of weather, but a number of school boards introduced such additional features as sliding doors, stalls, feed alleys, mangers, and a hayloft or the reservation of some corner of the stable for the storage of feed.

School stables had rather dark, foreboding,

and smelly interiors. They were draughty, unsanitary, and either too hot or too cold. The majority were cleaned irregularly and not too well, at that. Although everyone used the stable, no one considered it his duty to clean a stall or even to close the doors if he happened to be the last to leave. Sometimes the manure accumulated in such high mounds that the animals practically stood on their heads in their stalls. Nature, however, provided the flooring of the stall, so it was a matter of conjecture as to where the "floor" ended and the waste started.

Smaller children found it convenient to mount their horses inside the barn, where there were many supports that could be used to scramble up onto the backs of their mounts. Yet as the school term progressed, this became

Inside the school barn, that den of iniquity, at Bluffview S.D. in Alberta in 1956.

increasingly difficult to do. The temporary floor rose higher and higher with each day's accumulation of manure and straw, until a point was reached at which there was insufficient room for the child between the horse's back and the rafters. These little people had to find other means of mounting their horses outside the stable.

John Pearse, a pupil in the Namao S.D. (Namao, Alberta), thought he had the perfect solution to this ever-present problem of cleaning the barn. He sneaked along a supply of blasting caps to do the job. The resulting explosion blew the roof off the barn and gouged out a huge hole in the floor, but the manure was still there after the dust had settled. This "scientific" approach to cleaning the barn was never repeated, although the incident itself was considered worthy of recording in a chronicle about Namao S.D.

At the Garden Prairie S.D. (Granum, Alberta), the manure in the barn grew deeper and deeper as spring approached. It became more difficult each day to get the horses through the barn door. Harry Sahlen solved the problem in short order by sawing a couple of boards out of the top of the doorway.

Any activity that was considered of a questionable nature was held in the barn for fear the teacher would put an end to the entire affair if she knew what was taking place. This is why the barn was considered a den of iniquity if left unsupervised. It was the headquarters of the "stag club" when the weather was inclement. While the girls ate at their desks on such days, the boys repaired to the barn where, seated on the mangers, they ate their sandwiches while the horses munched their hay. The ammoniacal odour that permeated the barn was of no consequence to the group of hungry farm boys, whose appetites were keen after their morning chores and school games.

Many rural boys learned the habit of routinely visiting the barn rather than the outhouse in times of necessity. This practice was certainly not very hygenic, but considering the state of most outdoor privies during the winter, one could hardly blame them for their choice. At least the heat generated by the horses made the stable a bit more comfortable than the outhouse.

The custom of using the barn as a second privy for the males dictated that such places be out-of-bounds to all females. This was not always possible, as many girls drove or rode horses to school and had to enter the barn to take care of their animals. The boys soon learned to use a little discretion in such circumstances. Anytime a girl was seen approaching the barn, the boys inside were warned by an infallible system of signals from those on the outside. In other school systems, the girls got some preferential treatment: they were allowed to visit the barn before the boys at recess and at noon. Then the boys took over again.

When Margaret Befus was a student, the school barn was an important part of academic life.

I wonder who designed the school barn? There have been different styles in school design, but I have never seen a barn anywhere from Kempton to Key River that was not the same width, had a roof of the same pitch, and was not painted the same shade of red. The one at Kempton was a little longer than many others, having a garage and bins for wood and coal on the north end. Otherwise, it was basically fitted for six teams. The garage, to my knowledge, never held an automobile. It had double doors which were kept locked. The stage components, sawhorses, back drops, curtains, and all that was needed for the Christmas concert were stored here. I also believe the school and teacherage storm windows and screens spent half their time stored within those hallowed walls that I never entered.

The barn had no stalls but had a long manger extending down each side. On rainy days, it was an ideal place to play. Our favourite game was "Off the Ground," where we tried to see who could travel around the barn for the longest time without their feet touching the ground. You know, the two horses didn't even mind us travelling over their backs. I wonder if today's teachers or parents would approve of such a place to play?

In the thirties, students sometimes made the school barn part of their recreation equip-ment by climbing up on its sloped roof and sliding down.

When we played "Hide-and-Seek" we used it as a hiding place. The barn was also a great place to play "Ante-I-Over" as it did not have the steep pitch of the school roof nor the walls of windows awaiting a poor marksman.

Our teacher habitually visited her teacherage at lunchtime, leaving us to our own devices. One winter, the older boys congregated in Steve's caboose, lighting a fire and lunching in private. Private it was, until a girl told the teacher they were smoking. (She was rather a tomboy and perhaps did it because she was not included with the big boys.)

Every spring on Arbour Day, we cleaned the schoolyard, took down the storm windows, and cleaned the barn. I don't recall ever planting a tree, but in days before, someone had. The task of cleaning the barn was reserved for the big boys. That day, Steve arrived at school in a stoneboat with several manure forks. Normally, he kept his horses in one spot in the barn until the manure became too deep and then moved to the next stall.

In summer the horses were often let loose to graze, and woe betide the student who left the schoolyard gate open. School horses were always "homers!"

In the winter, when dances and social evenings were held in the schoolhouse, there was always a race to get your team in the barn as early as possible. During the evening, I recall, more than once, someone rushing into the classroom shouting, "Two horses are kicking and fighting in the barn!" The school would empty of men and boys, like saloons do in westerns at the sound of a shootout in the street. For this reason, my dad never put his

horses in the barn with all those strange animals. He unhitched them, tied them to the side of the sleigh, gave each an oat bundle, and covered them with horse blankets. They, at least, had a peaceful evening!

When Northland School Division was formed in Alberta, most of the school districts were consolidated. When the school barn no longer served its purpose, it was auctioned off to the highest bidder, and one more homesteader had a barn.

In the days before schoolyards were fenced, it was common practice to tether the horses wherever there was a plentiful supply of grass. The students who attended the Cuthbert S.D. 633 (Pierson, Manitoba) between 1892 and 1900 and travelled to school by horseback were in the habit of carrying a rope or light chain, a picket, and a mallet or heavy stick with which to drive the stake into the ground for foundation. Thus, the animal could be tethered wherever the grass grew most luxuriantly.

If any young attendant was careless in tying his horse or remiss in closing the school gate securely, the equine inevitably wandered off in the direction of home. It was quite a surprise for the folks on the homestead to look out the window and see the school horse in the middle of the afternoon, childless and buggyless, refreshing itself with a drink of cool water at the trough or merely standing in front of the barn, waiting for someone to let it in and feed it. Needless to add, the young driver had to hoof it all the way home to get the wayward animal and then ride back to school to retrieve the buggy. This was a most effective lesson against negligence, and the majority of school horses knew well how to teach it.

Many school districts, like the Uphill S.D. 3541 (High River, Alberta) and the River Junction S.D. (Lethbridge, Alberta), did not build barns, but used their schoolyards as corrals for the horses. Just as soon as the children arrived at the school, they unsaddled or unharnessed their beasts of burden and turned them loose to graze in the enclosure about the school. The scheme worked quite well in summer, as long as the fences were kept in a reasonable state of repair and no one forgot to close the main gate securely after coming into the yard. These schoolyards resembled the infields of rodeo grounds, for the moment school was dismissed at 3:30, the children assisted each other in cornering and catching their respective mounts.

Never Forgotten

At no time during the day were the horses in the barn completely forgotten. They had a way of communicating with those in the school. Their squealing, stamping, neighing, and general ruction were always a signal for some conscientious lad or lass to leave the lesson and investigate the cause for the rowdiness in the barn. Swarms of flies might be making life miserable for the animals; one of the horses might have gotten loose and be doing his best to annoy his moored companions; even an inquisitive snake, porcupine, badger, weasel, or skunk might have gained entrance to the barn. Sometimes it turned out that a blizzard was in the offing, and the psychic animals were giving the warning in the only way they knew how—by making noise. Not until the blizzard had swept over the district were the humans able to interpret the horses' urgent message.

To the children just beginning school, their horses were very special, particularly during the initial weeks of adjusting to this new life. It was always comforting for them to slip down to the barn or pasture and balance on the edge of the manger or fence beside their Maud, Buster, or whatever the animal was named. They never felt far from home or family with their pets nearby. Later on, when they were old enough to start driving, the school horse became a major responsibility, but for now, they were just a familiar friend.

Frances Whitney, a little first-grader in the River Junction S.D. (Lethbridge, Alberta), almost ruined a strategy for corralling horses because of her concern for her four-legged friends. One lovely afternoon, she requested permission to visit the privy, after which she decided the weather was far too nice for her immediate return to a dull classroom. Frances

Despite the presence of her older brothers, this little girl looks like she hasn't a friend in the world—it was her first day of school. But she, like many others, would likely find comfort in the familiar warmth of the Westra family's two school horses.

studied the six saddle horses grazing in the desert-like confines of the schoolyard, and concluded that the animals would be much happier if they were allowed to feed on the luxuriant growth of grass in the road allowance. With some difficulty, she opened the page-wire gate and let them out. The ponies liked their new-found freedom so much that they dispersed in various directions. This unexpected turn of events was most definitely not anticipated. Not knowing what to do next, she wandered back to the classroom, visibly shaken. Her white face and nervous condition alerted the teacher to the possibility that something was radically amiss. And it was! When the teacher discovered what Frances had done, the entire student body disappeared outside to assist in rounding up the horses. No one relished the idea of walking back home.

What happened to Frances for her part in the escapade? You guessed it! She received the first and only strapping of her entire school career. Today, after fifty years, Frances says, "Let me tell you, I've never forgotten that day!"

There were no screens on the windows or door of the Mona Lee S.D. (Veteran, Alberta) in 1920, so the horses used the windows as refuge from the nose flies. It was a real joy to see a student with his arm resting on his horse's neck doing his school work diligently. The pupils studied very hard and made excellent progress.

Let's Eat!

The noon-hour brought another surge of youngsters to the barn to feed their horses. Each child rushed outside and hauled the oat sheaf, sack of hay, or bag of oats from wherever it was and placed the food in the manger in front of the horse. The students were following the unwritten farmers' law that the livestock must be fed before man has a right to sit down to his own meal. As the children entered the stable, the horses turned their heads expectantly, snorted, flared their nostrils, and kicked their stalls. Soon all the animals were happily crunching and munching their lunch. In the dry thirties, their repast consisted mostly of prairie hay, slough grass, and Russian thistles, but the horses seemed to understand that they had to eat it or starve.

Socioeconomic status was often evident in the barn at feeding time. Some horses were fed oats or green feed; others, prairie hay; a few had to be content with straw; others went hungry. The lunches the children ate in the

In good weather, the Newell S.D. 3005 (Coronation, Alberta) ''cafeteria'' was a buggy. The lunches are a good indication of changing times: one boy holds a sugar sack; another, a new-style lunch box; and a third, a Swift's Lard pail.

All aboard! The entire Olive S.D. (Hanna, Alberta) in 1933 going home by means of a single team and democrat.

schoolhouse often exhibited a parallel inequality. Horses and youngsters alike were soon educated to the fact that they were living in a world divided into "haves" and "have-nots."

Louise Kuebler's school horse, Neddy, was black, part Shetland and part Welsh. She loved Neddy dearly, though he was often rather unpopular at Royston School around lunch time.

Once we had arrived at school in the cart, we turned Neddy loose in the schoolyard, making him available for anyone wishing to ride him. Ofttimes, someone would forget to take his lard lunch pail into the school, and if Neddy found it, he demolished the container and ate the lunch, making him rather unpopular with that pupil for the rest of the day. I don't think he ever bothered an empty lunch pail.

Hazel (Swalm) Cahoon's first recollection of school horses is of the students taking their lunches out to the barn and sitting backwards on the horses' rumps and using the stable's cross-beams for tables. The place was seldom cleaned, and the horses' rear ends came very close to the beams before anything was ever done about it. Hazel always used to find it

53

very exciting when, every five years or so, you could see the floor boards of the stalls.

It was common practice for the students to visit the barn briefly during recess to checkup on their animals. Experience had taught these boys and girls not to take too much for granted and that labour, thought, and perseverance were the attributes of successful living. The knowledge that Old Faithful was safe and content always brought a glow of contentment to the consciencious child.

The students again converged on the barn at 3:30, this time with more vim-and-vigour than on any of the previous occasions. School was out, and freedom was theirs to enjoy. The horses, sensing they were homeward bound, caught the excitement and contributed their share to the air of long-awaited emancipation. Each outfit, when assembled, paused momentarily in front of the school to pick up its passengers and freight and then rattled out of the yard onto the multi-rutted road to the accompaniment of the churnlike rumbles of the horse's stomach. Soon only tiny puffs of dust dotted the countryside, marking the homeward progress of the children. The school day had come to an end! Bereft of its human life and spirit, the Little White Schoolhouse stood silent and desolate against the evening sky, seemingly awaiting the return of the teacher and the boys and girls on the morrow for the next phase of their educational programme.

6 | Teacher's Pet

Most teachers at rural schools were not horsemen by any stretch of the imagination. Usually, their first experience with horses coincided with their first teaching experience. Yet in spite of their misgivings at the start, some became quite adept at handling horses. The rest tolerated the beasts of burden for the simple reason that they supplied the only ready means of transportation. These teachers were sometimes described as not knowing one end of the horse from the other, and these inexperienced rural pedagogues invariably placed themselves in unique predicaments when left alone to handle the horses.

After a single demonstration, Hilda, the teacher at George S.D. 1386 (Lestock, Saskatchewan), was left on her own to bridle the horse, back it between the shafts, and hitch up the buggy. Her passenger, a six-year-old girl, was much too small to be of any assistance. Hilda was no lover of horses—in fact, she was terrified of them. However, she was duty-bound to perform the task of hitching up the horse to the buggy in spite of her distaste for the chore. On the way home, she noticed that the horse appeared to be going in circles and surmised that it must have contracted some sort of disease that made it act in such a peculiar manner. As the school was located atop a hill, the trip down was perilous, with the horse reeling all the way. When they reached the bottom, Hilda decided to get out and investigate the cause of this strange conduct. As it turned out, she had fastened both reins to one side of the bridle!

Mr. W.R. Urling came to teach in the Daly Creek S.D. 1076 (Granum, Alberta) around 1910. Having been a city dweller, the teacher's ignorance of country living and peculiar behaviour convinced the students that he was stupid. He bought himself an old saddle horse and named him Hell Tornado. It was his practice to hook the horse to the buggy, climb into the vehicle, stand on the floor with knees bent, and holler, "Hell, Tornado!" He'd slap

The three Thuroo children travelled with their teacher to Melbrae S.D. (Youngstown, Alberta) every day in 1934 in a two-wheeler, commonly known as a carriole or sulky. It was crowded!

the horse smartly on the rump with the reins, and the animal would start out at a gallop and run all the way home.

One day, the kids rotated the wheels of the buggy, moving the high back wheels to the front and the small front wheels to the back. Mr. Urling drove the buggy that way (looking all the while as if he was going uphill) until the weekend, when a neighbour needed the vehicle to go to town. He returned the wheels to their proper places.

Sexual Education the Rural Way

Albert Ganser did not have a great deal of experience with horses, but he needed a horse to get to the Rosenheim S.D. 1892 (Provost, Alberta) in the 1939/40 school year. But when his mare had a colt at school one day, both he and his students picked up some veterinary knowledge pretty quickly.

It was a one-room school, and since I had three miles to go, I covered the distance in a cutter in winter with a team named Babe and Ruby. With no snow removal equipment available, the roads were very poor. The rural mailman from Provost delivered the mail out

this way, about a twenty-mile trip. On numerous occasions, after ploughing through heavy snowdrifts, his team was nearly exhausted by the time he reached the Rosenheim School. We made an arrangement that Babe and Ruby would finish the trip while he left his worn-out team in the school barn. Then, after they had a good rest, we made the exchange on the return part of his trip. Now they were raring to go again!

In this same year at Rosenheim School, the boys came in at recess and excitedly told me that Ruby had given birth to a colt. The situation was astounding not only for the children, who were vibrating with excitement, but also for me. Imagine, not having a colt early in the

The only sex education for youngsters in the days of the Little White Schoolhouse was in the barn. Greg Gordon travelled to Rose Lynn S.D. (Rose Lynn, Alberta) with two horses: mare and foal.

morning, then suddenly, here it is! I went out to the barn to check out the situation. The wood was piled up in one of the vacant stalls, forming sort of an inclined plane from the floor. The little colt lay on the highest part of the oblique section near the roof of the barn, full of pep and vinegar for being only about an hour old. The harness was still on Ruby, but this didn't seem to affect the delivery of her little one.

Stella Johnson, the teacher in the Fife S.D. (Carnduff, Saskatchewan) in 1922, couldn't permit studies or propriety to interfere with her concern for the well-being of Doll, her school pony. One of Stella's grade two pupils, a lad with whom she rode to school, dashed into the room one day and breathlessly announced, "Please, Teacher, old Doll is having a colt!" What could the teacher do? She knew she couldn't cope with such a maternity case; her past veterinary experience had been very limited and, furthermore, had never included a blessed event of the horse variety. Cats? Yes. Chickens? Yes. But horses? Never! In spite of her feelings of inadequacy, Stella rushed out with the troubled lad to see what could be done. Her oldest pupils appeared to know what to do, and a neighbouring farmer, who had been hurriedly summoned by one of the students, soon came to their rescue. The mare survived, but they lost the colt. Thirteen amateur midwives, somewhat sadder and much wiser, dawdled back to the classroom to resume their study of books.

Teachers Cared About Students . . . and Horses!

Teachers sometimes went far beyond the call of duty out of concern for their students—and their students' horses!

This kind of caring made a difference—a practical, physical difference, of course, but there was something more: by recognizing and sharing a student's concern for his horse, the teacher encouraged that very quality in all his students.

One boy and his sister drove a distance of seven miles to reach the Pleasant Lake S.D. (Whitecourt, Alberta). They were hardy individuals, and neither the uncertainties of the weather nor the long drive held any terrors for them. Through all types of weather—rain, snow, heat, cold—they could always be expected to be present and on time.

The girl was also a great lover of animals, particularly horses. One cold, blustery day in 1940, the two rode to school together on one horse. On arriving at the school, the horse was wringing wet from the hard and fast ride. The girl, hestitating, tied the horse to the

One balmy spring day in 1933 in the Pine Valley S.D. (Tawatinaw, Alberta), a curious school horse wandered into the school's open cloakroom. He was considered a smart animal, but he had considerable difficulty in extricating himself from these cramped quarters.

usual post and went indoors. She was worried lest the animal catch cold and was not at all certain she had done the right thing in leaving the perspiring horse out in the bitterly cold wind.

Sure enough, when she went out to investigate a few minutes later, the horse was shivering badly. There were no barns nearby, so she asked her teacher, Mr. Perrich, if she could bring her pony into the classroom for a short while to dry. This was a most extraordinary request, and the teacher realized that it contravened not only school rules, but health regulations as well. Since the girl was so deeply concerned about her pet, however, he discarded his officialdom and permitted her to bring in the horse.

It wasn't long before the pony relieved itself on the school floor. The girl, without shame or hesitation, immediately took care of the situation, and within the hour, the pony was warm and dry enough to resume his rightful place outside. This display of benevolence on the part of both the girl and her teacher left everyone feeling very happy.

Even after the crisis was over, Margaret Mace's teacher at the Collins S.D. probably suffered no regret over his quick actions. He did not have to wonder if he had made a difference that day!

We lived three and a half miles from the Collins S.D. (Lousana, Alberta). Most of the time we drove to school in a one-horse cart our dad had made. In the spring, the runoff caused the sloughs to rise beyond the level of the road, and one day, our poor horse lost his footing in the water. Down he went. The shafts of the cart held him, and no amount of struggling or assistance could free him. Our teacher, John Mayell, waded into the icy water and undid the harness to let faithful old Charlie back up on his feet. The knee-high, laced boots our teacher wore, his pride and joy, were ruined. They had cost him all of his first paycheque—fifteen dollars.

Rural teachers could do much to see that school ponies received humane treatment from their youthful proprietors. The best method of encouraging proper treatment was for the pedagogue to handle his own horse in an exemplary manner. Unfortunately, this practice was not always observed.

Tom, a teacher in the Potter Creek S.D. (Rimbey, Alberta), purchased Ginger, a black thoroughbred horse, to ride to school during the winter months. Jonathon Fuller, the former owner, was very proud of Ginger and had misgivings about selling him when the family returned to the United States in 1913. He had raised Ginger from a colt in Montana before coming to Alberta to take up a homestead. Ginger was sleek looking, of gentle disposition, a fast trotter, and an excellent saddle or buggy horse.

The poor animal fell into bad hands when purchased by the teacher. One day while Ginger was fastened to the school fence, some children started pitching snowballs at him. The horse became frightened and jerked back on the bridle. This in itself would have had no serious consequences, but Tom had carelessly left the bridle in a twisted position on the horse's head. As a result, a buckle cut deeply into one eye and blinded Ginger. From then on, the horse wasted away until, in time, he resembled a hide stretched over a pile of bones—quite a contrast to the Ginger who was once a nice sleek horse, full of life.

At last the teacher sold the animal to a man who mercifully had it shot. Ginger's former owner inquired about him regularly in letters written to friends in the Potter Creek district. Mr. Fuller always mentioned that he regretted selling such a fine thoroughbred. No one had the heart to inform him of Ginger's sad fate. Although he eventually learned of the animal's death, it was never explained that his untimely end was brought about by sheer carelessness and indifference on the part of the teacher.

That Horse Had Never Been Ridden Before

Ray Tanton taught school in Saskatchewan in 1923, before the automobile came into common use. There were a few in operation, but mostly for pleasure—Sundays, holidays, or special occasions.

My first school was Pheasant Plains School in the Blackwood area of Saskatchewan. I had arranged for someone to meet the harvest excursion train when it arrived from Winnipeg at the Sintaluta station. Harry Meek, one of the district locals, drove up to the station to fetch me with a buckboard and a team of spirited horses.

Coming from Charlottetown, Prince Edward Island—The Garden of the Gulf—

this country was brand new to me. It was exciting to ride over the wide open prairie, so totally different from my home. I was again thrilled when, rounding a wooded bluff, we entered a coulee which led into the Qu'Appelle Valley. It spread expansively before us, its wide bottom covered with fields of grain.

I boarded at a ranch a short distance from the edge of the valley and two or three miles from the school—a distance I considered too far to walk. My neighbour lent me a little Indian pony, which was one of a band of captured wild horses. It was tiny, but wiry. In fact,

Usually, a teacher gets a shiny, red apple, but the teacher at Springbank S.D. (Calgary, Alberta) in 1907, Isabelle M. Lawson, was presented with this horse.

if I leaned over while in the saddle, I could touch the ground with my foot. The first time I mounted him, he bucked a few times and then galloped away. Anytime I reined him in, he'd throw his head back and strike me on the chin. Nevertheless, in time we became accustomed to one another, and a friendship soon developed.

My boarding house belonged to a bachelor farmer whose housekeeper was an elderly Swiss lady. She found it difficult to manage with a boarder, so I moved in with another family, Bernie and his wife and son. Here too, I had to ride to school.

Fortunately, I was allowed the use of Bernie's farm horse for the time being. He was plump, with a broad back, and had no saddle. I remember the first time I rode him. I carried my lunch pail in my left hand, and when I rested it on his mane and jumped to mount him, he suddenly swerved toward me, frightened by the pail. I sailed right over him, landing abruptly on the opposite side on all fours. The next time, Bernie held on to the horse until I mounted, then handed the pail to me. The instant my pail rattled (due to a jar of jam inside), the horse jumped ahead, flying straight out from under me and dumping me on the seat of my pants on the ground. I finally left my lunch pail with Bernie and managed to reach school without incident. It wasn't until later that I was told the horse had never been ridden before.

Right after this incident, I had an even wilder pony. He would shy at a leaf blown across the road by the wind, almost unseating me. One morning as I rode to school, I came near a coulee that crossed the road. The animal stopped dead in his tracks and wouldn't budge an inch further. Something ahead had annoyed him. I got off, tied him to the fence, and walked ahead to see what had spooked him. There was a team of horses down in the coulee hitched to an upside-down grain wagon with the wheels aloft. I heard a groan emanating from beneath it. I yelled down to him that I'd get him right out. His pathetic voice replied, "There's no hurry. I've been here all night!" The patient victim lay under the box with a wheat seeder pinning him down. I unhitched the horses, tied them to the fence, and attempted to roll the wagon box off him. Just then, two school boys happened along with a buggy. I transported him to a neighbouring farm, leaving the boys to bring the horses.

Down in the valley, a family operated a coal mine, digging the rock out from the cutbank of the valley. The father had been a miner in Wales and knew his job. He had pit props and all the fixings needed to carry on his work. The horses who pulled coal carts out of the mine wore helmets to protect their heads from bumping against the low ceilings of the mine shaft. Four children in this family attended school, riding horseback, two to a horse. This was ideal during the summer; however, in winter, especially when the temperature dropped below zero and was accompanied by strong winds, it was too stormy and cold to ride. The family overcame this problem with their "hunting sleigh" invention, a square box mounted on runners with a top and trap door. An escape hatch was located at the rear which could be quickly opened by manipulating a rope. The lines passed through an opening in the front, which also served as a window. The miner's children used this method of transportation in winter no matter what the weather was like. They were thus well protected from the wind and storms.

One of the girls in the school rode a pony that was very skittish. In fact, he kicked at anything that came near him. The horse was kept in the first stall inside the door of the barn. After several of the children were almost kicked by him, I had her put the animal in the back stall where it would not be necessary for the youngsters to walk behind him. The child's father went wild! He maintained that the front stall was theirs and they were going to keep it, and I was given orders to that effect. Of course, the safety of the children was paramount, so needless to say, I kept the capricious horse in the back stall.

In those early days, girls were more discrete than they are now. They wore bloomers over their skirts when riding horseback and removed them before entering the classroom. To annoy me, the man made his daughter leave her skirt at home and wear the bloomers into class. This was unheard of and was considered extremely bold. I belonged to the old school and deemed it proper to maintain correct behaviour, so I sent her home to dress properly. The school board backed me up as did the Department of Education in Regina. When the family phoned the registrar, his response was, "Dress the child properly!"

On one occasion, a school dance was being held in a neighbouring teaching institution. I was invited, so I saddled my horse and set out to join them. Normally, a boy took his girlfriend along. Customarily, he would ride up to her door to pick her up, and she would come out, wearing bloomers over her skirt, hop up behind him, and ride double to their destination. As I didn't have a girl to take, I was alone on the trip. It was a cold, clear night in winter, with a bright moon shining above. Because I was attending a dance, I didn't wear my moccasins, but a pair of leather shoes and rubber galoshes. I soon realized my mistake and got off to walk to keep my feet from freezing. I planned to lead the horse, but he would have none of this. He pulled backward and

Even the teachers had to bundle up. Marguerite (Hittle) Warner arrives home on school horse June in the dead of winter in 1943 from Collingwood S.D. 1873 (Wimborne, Alberta) with a load of books. It was a cold three-mile trip.

even reared up. The only thing to do was to tie the lines to the horn and drive him with one hand. This was an awkward position but possible. In spite of the brilliant moonlight, I soon lost my way, so I permitted the horse to have his head. In no time, he stopped at the gate behind the barn. We were home!

standest meekly by; With thy proudly arched and glossy neck, and dark and fiery eyes."

I was a country school teacher in the twenties and early thirties; Flirt was a dark brown mare with dapples, part standard bred and part thoroughbred. I could ride her with or without a saddle, or I could hitch her to a

"She Can Ride From Heaven to ———"

When Madge (Rogers) McCullough bought Flirt in 1926, she had no idea they would have only four short years together. Flirt left her with many wonderful memories, though.

One of life's most beautiful happenings is to own and love a horse: To get on its back, to feel a "oneness" with its strength and speed as you canter joyously down a country road or gallop madly across the prairie. You almost have the same feeling of expectation as the horse when you hear that soft "whinny" when a feed of oats is on the way! Anyone who has loved a horse can understand the Arab who said, "My beautiful! My beautiful! that

Madge (Rogers) McCullough in daring riding knickers riding bareback on Flirt in 1926.

buggy or cutter and drive her. Sometimes we harnessed Flirt with another horse and drove them as a team. She was so quiet and gentle that children could easily handle and ride her. She was a most important chapter in the book of my life.

I bought Flirt from Oscar Glaze of Francis, Saskatchewan, in 1926. I had ridden her while teaching at Ferguslea School and had fallen very much in love with her. Mrs. Glaze wrote to me that they would sell Flirt for sixty dollars if I were interested. Was I? "I am! I am! I am!" I quickly replied.

I had to ride Flirt from Francis to my parents' home near Wawota. I gathered together sixty dollars (quite a sum in those days), borrowed a saddle, clothed myself in riding knickers (a daring thing to do in 1926), and with the bridle over my arm, caught the Canadian Pacific Railway passenger train from Manor to Francis.

Mrs. Glaze met me, and the deal was swiftly transacted. Next morning, very early, I saddled my very own horse and began the thrilling—but long—ride home! The first day, I rode as far as Howard, where I spent the night with friends, the Murdock MacKenzies. It was fairly dark when I arrived, but Mr. MacKenzie helped me to unsaddle and tend to Flirt.

Next morning at breakfast, my host greeted me with, "That's some horse! I don't know what you paid for her, but I'll give you twice as much if you sell her to us!"

"Oh, no I can't!" I quickly replied. Of course I wouldn't have, but nevertheless, I felt proud that he approved of my purchase.

Flirt had developed a saddle sore from the previous day's long, tiring ride. I was so concerned that I had the MacKenzies send the saddle home, by express, and I rode the animal bareback the rest of the way. Needless to say, it wasn't Flirt who had the sores by the time we arrived home. Ouch!

When Flirt was in the pasture, I could walk up to her, clutch her mane, and jump onto her back. She would immediately head for the barn, where I put the bridle on her. Of course, there were always a few handfuls of oats in my pockets and a few more in her bin.

One time my mother, who was not the best horsewoman in the world, drove Flirt to visit a neighbour some seven miles away. When Mr. Hancock tied Flirt to the fence, the bit slipped out of her mouth and was left dangling under her chin. When it was time to leave, Mother untied her and proceeded home, passing through whatever gates and by whatever rigs she met. Nearing home, Mr. George Weatherald stopped her and returned the bit to Flirt's mouth, saying, "You really shouldn't drive a horse without a bit in its mouth!" Mother was astounded and was full of praise for such a trustworthy horse.

In 1927, I began teaching at the Model S.D. 931. The school was only seven miles from my parents' home, so I boarded at home and rode to school every day. What wonderful, wonderful rides I had. In winter I left home before the sun rose and returned home in the evening after the sun had set. Never have I enjoyed sunrises and sunsets as much as I did during those two years, nor has there been such a close feeling between horse and rider.

Oh, those rides, shifting through the seasons, in all kinds of weather! In spring I spotted the first blade of green grass, the first pussy willows, and the first crocus; I would nod to the first meadow lark and wave to the first crow seen on the northeast side of Moose Mountain. I watched the fresh buds grow into leaves on the various trees along the way. In autumn I sighted hints of reds and yellows that soon burst into magnificence and finally watched them blow away on chilly winds that brought the first flakes of snow. I hunched my shoulders against the bitter cold as Flirt and I plunged through heavy snowdrifts.

One morning, as my mother handed me my riding quirt, she broke into verse, saying:

"There was a young teacher of Model,
Who rode horseback exceedingly well.
With saddle and quirt,
On a horse named Flirt,
She can ride from heaven to ———"
(You know where!)

I chuckled all the way to school that morning.

Ruth (Nordal) Currie drove Darky to Yunghill S.D. (Bulyea, Saskatchewan) from 1943 to 1946. "His colour had lightened over the years until he was almost white. This was a source of amusement to the children, as 'Darky' hardly suited him."

Flirt had a bay coloured filly in 1929 called Mickey. She was never as reliable as her mother. She would shy and balk and even pitch her rider off when inclined to do so. As a baby, she kicked at me every time I climbed onto Flirt's back and even tried to boot me while I was riding.

In 1930, Flirt was struck and killed by lightning. We found her in the pasture with a long burn mark down her front leg. She must have been running with her head outstretched, her legs in full action. My two brothers buried her where she fell, near the top of a small hill, west of the old farm home.

There is some continuity to this history, for Mickey's colts eventually became saddle horses for my own children.

7 | Horse Sense

"Hec" + "Dis" 1911

The school horse was an intelligent creature, and teachers, in periods of despondency, often thought that they would do better, educationally, if they had the horses in the schoolroom and the students in the barn. School ponies seemed to comprehend the daily routine only too well. If the students were not dismissed promptly at 3:30, the animals in the barn displayed such restlessness that the sounds of their discontent carried right to the schoolhouse. The champing, pawing, stamping, kicking, and whinnying were enough to break the firm resolve of any teacher to keep the children after school. When the horses were permitted to graze in the schoolyard, it wasn't unusual to see some old codger of a horse peer solicitously through the window, as if to announce, "You know, it's time to dismiss school!" These quadrupeds appeared to have some sixth "horse sense" that enabled them to judge the passage of time quite accurately. Horses were known to rip off a gate latch or a barn door fastening just to alert the young driver that it was time to leave.

Class Dismissed!

One day after school, the Mowers children hitched their horse, Biddy, to the buggy and were preparing to climb in when she trotted off for home. Down the road she ran and into the barnyard, all clearly visible from the school as their home was on a hill just one mile away. Within minutes, the children saw the same buggy re-emerge from the yard with Dad in the driver's seat and head toward the school. Biddy came at a sharp trot, picked up the children in the schoolyard, and made the return trip in jig time. Doubtless, the children received a lecture on paying attention.

Ethel (Doyle) Christensen thought the main goal in life of her horse, Peanuts, was to teach her some horse sense. Peanut's efforts did make a difference, though, and not just to Ethel: Peanuts even taught her teacher a lesson!

Peanuts, when born, was the colour of a well-roasted peanut but turned to a mousy brown. His mane, tail, ears, hooves, and eyes were coal black. This animal was raised to be one of Dad's farm horses, but he had a cunning, lazy streak in him and let us know that he much preferred to be a kid's school pony by pulling all kinds of tricks to escape work.

I was a frail, timid child and suffered leg-aches often, so I was never permitted to walk the two miles to school even though my brothers and sisters occasionally did. Peanuts, therefore, became *my* horse, and he soon proved himself to be a reliable child's horse —as a rule, but not always.

Peanuts had his own way of adding spice to his life and usually had a very satisfied look on his long, slim face after one of his tricks. Peanuts was never mean, and he never tried to buck us younger kids off. He played the role of Cupid with one of his acts, but his real intention was to teach me some horse sense. How well I remember that day!

I was just starting grade three when he left me to walk home alone. I had been kept in after school for talking, so when all the other horses had been picked up, he decided not to wait for me. He had an uncanny ability to slip his halter over his small ears no matter how tight the jaw strap was. Once this was accomplished, he was on his way, as the barn door had been left open.

It was a nice day in late September so, once out of the schoolyard, he stopped to enjoy the nice tall grass along the roadside. With no big brother or sister to help me catch him, I was pretty upset. My new teacher, Miss Pearl

Stewart, was a farm girl and didn't foresee any big chore in catching my horse. She locked up the one-room Union School as I ran to get the halter from the barn.

Peanuts let us walk within ten feet of him, pretending he didn't see us. Talking kindly to him, I took another step forward. He raised his head, which he shook as if to say, "Oh no you don't!", then trotted off down the road a few more rods and began grazing again. Miss Stewart and I trailed behind him in this manner for half a mile! I was getting madder and madder every time he refused to let me get close enough to grab his mane. It was as if he was saying, "I'll see you home, but you are going to walk!"

By now, we were at the crossroad where my teacher should have branched toward her boarding place. The prospect of meeting up with the range cattle all by myself terrified me; I also knew that if I did manage to catch Peanuts I would not get on his bare back without a saddle or fence on which to climb. I raised such a fuss, there seemed nothing she could do but continue on with me, hoping for a miracle.

Luckily for both of us, before we had gone much further, a car came up from behind us. My big brother Ed was driving. I'm sure Miss Stewart was just as glad as I was to see any member of my family just then. He stopped and asked, "What's going on here?" I introduced them, but it was Miss Stewart who explained why I was late in leaving school and how she didn't expect it to be such a chore to catch a horse. "You'll never catch that one

Ethel Christensen and the other students at the Woodval S.D. (Vermilion, Alberta) in

1933. Ethel is riding Peanuts.

with a rope in your hands!" Ed said. Then he turned to me and, in spite of my tear-streaked face, said, "Serves you right, you little nut! I should let you walk home for talking in school, but Dad would have a piece of my hide, so you'd better jump in . . . in the back! I'm going to take your teacher home, now that you have taken her out of her way!"

That was the beginning of their friendship, and at Easter time, she became my sister-in-law.

I often wondered if Peanuts didn't teach Miss Stewart a bigger lesson than he did me, as she never kept any of her pupils in after school again if she could punish us with a missed recess or noon hour.

The school pony was also often much keener than the scholars to be off to school. One cold, blustery morning, Ken Winter hitched old Roaney to the jumper, drove her to the front of the house, tied the reins to the peg on the dashboard, then hurried into the house to put on his heavy coat. Ken's little sister carried out the lunch pails and an armful of robes, returning to assist Ken with the hot stones that were to be used as footwarmers on their trip to Wolf Willow S.D. (Merid, Saskatchewan). Just at that instant, their mother shouted, "Run! Run! Roaney is leaving!" Ken had taken off his jacket and was without his cap or big coat, but when his mother sounded the alarm, he rushed out, just as he was, to pursue Roaney and the jumper.

The horse must have been in a teasing mood, for she kept enticing him to within hailing distance—not too far ahead to dis-

courage Ken from continuing the race, but yet far enough to prevent him from catching up—then racing away again. The lad continued his pursuit for a quarter of a mile, into a biting north wind, then quit. By this time, his ears were frozen stiff, so he dashed back home, meeting his mother and sister on the way. His mother also gave up the chase as her legs, protected only by cotton stockings, had become badly frostbitten. Ken's sister remained in the race to within half a mile of the school, when two of the older pupils met her and took her aboard their buggy. Roaney

On a cold morning, neither Bobby Durant nor his school horse were anxious to start on the four-and-a-half-mile ride to Rye S.D.

travelled right to the Wolf Willow School! The teacher, alarmed at the sight of the empty jumper, sent some of the bigger boys back with Roaney and the sled to investigate. The little girl had covered over a mile and a half before she was picked up, but as she had been warmly clothed, she did not suffer from the cold. Ken, on the other hand, was forced to stay home for several days as his frostbitten ears had ballooned to three times their normal size.

Once in a while an adult decided to give the children a treat and show them how to drive to school. Such days were red-letter occasions, but that did not mean they would be free of the frowns of fortune. The grownups had their fair share of annoying incidents whenever they volunteered their help.

Mr. Wilson of the White Rose S.D. 365 (Windthorst, Saskatchewan) was one such adult. On the coldest mornings, he drove his children to school. Relieved of all responsibilities, the Wilson scholars invariably enjoyed these none-too-frequent joyrides. They loved to watch their father's team of thoroughbreds as they plunged up to their backs in the fresh snowdrifts. Mr. Wilson was at his most cheerful self on these rare occasions as well and brightened the journey by lustily singing "We're off to Philadelphia in the Morning" or some such appropriate ditty.

One morning, just before starting for school, he went into the house for a moment to warm his hands. The horses were left untied at the door. In a flash, they slipped away of their own accord and bolted past the house and down the road they knew so well. A neighbour girl, walking the same road, heard the clatter of hooves behind her and stepped aside, hoping to get a ride. But not this time! Strange that the Wilsons should pass her by. But look—it was an unmanned team! What had happened?

The thoroughbreds cleared the school gateposts neatly and came to a sudden halt, the tongue of the cutter crashing loudly into the barn door. The teacher, busily engaged in preparing the day's lessons, went out to investigate. She immediately tied up the sweating horses in the barn and sent one of the students back down the road to discover the whereabouts of the Wilson family. The eager chargers had deprived Mr. Wilson of singing his rousing songs that particular morning!

To School, but No Further

Almost any equine devoted to taking children or teachers to school became known as a school horse, and they soon acquired a strong aversion to travelling any distance longer than that to the school. Try to drive your school pony to the post office or any other place on

Saturday or Sunday, and invariably it necessitated acute effort to keep the animal from turning in at the school gate. The horse often remained bitter for the rest of the trip. It's no wonder they say you spoil a horse by converting him into a school horse.

Zadie, the Weigum family's school pony, was assigned the task of taking the Weigum and Yost families' cream to the CNR station in Trochu. Zadie was considered trustworthy enough for the two women since she had proven herself to be with school children. But Zadie had no liking for such a menial chore. Her mission in life was to make sure the Weigum children received their education. She decided she would go no further than the Fairmount S.D. (Trochu, Alberta). Zadie balked, kicked, took to the ditch, and pulled a few more tricks she had learned as a school horse. In spite of all this twisting, obstructing, and putting grit in the machine, Zadie discovered she had two very ambitious women to contend with. With Mrs. Weigum leading her by the halter and Mrs. Yost in the buggy slapping Zadie's rump continuously, she very ignominiously delivered the cream to the railway station.

The return trip found Zadie a horse of another colour. Her step was lively, she had her direction right, and she had lost all interest in the "seat of learning." She sped by the white building without even a backward glance. Zadie had long been a favourite at Fairmount School, but this day she lost grace in the eyes of the three Yost offspring, who had hoped for a ride after a session with the books.

Even Horses Need a Break

Strange as it may appear, Star, Bob, and Clayt knew just as well as the children that Saturday and Sunday were not school days. It was a herculean task to harness a school pony and hitch him to a buggy on a Saturday. What a contrast to Monday mornings when the horse understood the necessity for the trip and became calm, co-operative, and willing to go to school!

Of course, not all ponies were of such an agreeable disposition. Some were no more eager than humans to give up their freedom on Monday mornings. Often someone had to rise an hour earlier on Mondays to catch the pony after its weekend of liberty. Usually the subject wasn't hard to catch when found, but the search invariably ended in the farthest corner of the pasture. The horse usually stood quietly watching as the young master drew near, bridle dangling along in the dust and oats rustling in an old pail. Some horses, though, could not be caught in this fashion but had to be lassoed or corralled.

Weekends didn't really mean a holiday for the Garriott's school horse—he had to entertain all four little Garriotts. He loved it, though.

Marjorie, the oldest girl, taught him to kneel, but only her would he accommodate.

When Barbara (Dawe) Melling began teaching at Kedleston S.D. (Vernon, British Columbia), she purchased a horse named Brownie to ride back and forth from home each day, rather than batch at the teacherage. Brownie turned out to be a law unto himself.

Over the weekends, my younger sister and brother alternated hauling sacks of hay to school so Brownie would have something to eat while in the barn each day. Well, that animal knew the weekend was his time off, and what a job they had persuading him to haul the hay to the school! He'd plant all four hooves firmly on the ground and refuse to budge. A lot of apples, carrots, potatoes, and the like were used to entice him at the start of each journey.

Once school was out at the end of June, Brownie had the freedom of the pasture for the summer and was ridden very little. On the first school day of the second term, a lot of coaxing was required to get him underway. I had dismissed the students with their lists of supplies to be purchased and was busy getting ready for the first full day when I heard a frightful noise in the vicinity of the barn. A moment later, I saw my horse galloping past the window toward home.

I couldn't understand how he could have broken the railing barring the doorway. Upon investigation, I discovered Brownie had scraped a hole in the dirt with his front hooves, lowered himself to his knees, lifted the bar, and escaped, the railing falling back into place. I quickly changed into my slacks in preparation for the four-mile walk which

lay ahead. I knew the horse would go straight home and expected the sight of a riderless horse appearing at the farm would cause my parents a great deal of anxiety.

Just then, I heard a car honk and looked out to see the father of one of my pupils arrive with my horse in tow behind his car. He had met up with Brownie on a very narrow section of the road lined with bushes and parked his car right across the road to prevent him from getting by. Fortunately, he also carried a rope in his car, which he tied to Brownie's halter; the horse was thus captured and returned to the school.

I mounted my horse and reached home in record time as Brownie insisted on running all the way. He wasn't any more eager about that first day of school than the children were! He certainly knew which day was which.

Pearl, the gentle black mare in this story, hauled the Jensen children to Hammer S.D. (Olds, Alberta) for many years. Teamed with Buck or Daisy, she willingly pulled the trim buggy, up to five Jensens, and any other young neighbours who needed a lift along the two-and-a-half-mile route to school. Come summer, though, Pearl felt she deserved a break.

"Papa, can we ride Pearl?"

"If you catch her, you can ride her!" challenged their father.

It was 1935. The children were in the middle of summer holidays, and boredom had reared its head. The three youngsters set about capturing the old black mare, but she knew very well it was holiday time. Ten months of pulling a buggy full of children to and from school had earned her a rest. Hence, she had no interest in the fresh grass they offered her, and she was too wise to be fooled by an empty bucket. Yet the smell of oats brought her close enough for the boy to put on the halter. A few pushes on her hefty sides towards the pole fence enabled the agile children to leap on the broad back.

Out of the yard and onto the flat dirt road Pearl trotted, with the tots bouncing gently on her back. There were no deep ditches in those days, and the grass grew down the middle of the soft dirt road. Trees and bushes lined the fences, and daisies and goldenrod mingled with the lush grass.

The horse trotted willingly up and down the road, the youngsters laughing and chattering, happy that they had something to while away their sunny day. Pearl began snatching mouthfuls of grass, her trot became a walk, and with head down, she moved slower and slower until she finally stopped altogether.

"Get up! Get up! Get up, Pearl!" the children shouted. Pearl went on eating, ignoring their pleas.

"Come on, Lazybones!" cried the angry boy, pulling on the halter shank in an attempt to drag the horse away from the grass.

"Let's try kicking her!" Three pairs of bare heels began drumming on the hard stomach. The black head rose, the ears swept back, and Pearl began to trot.

The boy suddenly realized just what the mare had in mind. Pulling on the halter with all his might, he hollered, "Whoa! Whoa! Whoa, Pearl!"

Pearl paid no attention whatsoever. She directed her attention to the telephone pole down the road. Carefully judging the distance, she paced her trot, gently and efficiently wiping all three riders off her back against the pole. The children fell in a heap on the warm ground.

"Darn you, Pearl!" screamed the boy, wiping a trickle of blood from his nose. The girls were in tears, one holding her head, the other rubbing her wrist. A few yards down the road, Pearl munched on the sweet summer grass, her long back tail swishing the flies away.

Some horses, of course, just didn't know when to quit. Bill Thomson attended the Ridgeview S.D. 489 (Gladys, Alberta). It took a while for his horse, Dick, to understand that his job was not to stand in the school pasture all day, but to take his master to school.

The horse I rode was a retired cow pony by the name of Dick. He had spent his younger years working on ranches in the Pekisko area, mostly at the 7U (Brown's). The usual procedure was to turn Dick loose in the enclosure at night and catch him in the morning for the trip to school.

Come the first of July, I didn't need him, so I didn't bother to catch him. About a quarter to nine, he took off on his own and covered the mile and a half to school. Of course, there were no other horses there. Even so, he went into the pasture and patiently waited until about 3:30, then came back home. The horse did this for three or four days, until he finally decided that since nobody else was going to school, there wasn't much point in him going either.

No Driver Required

Once in a while, school ponies were entrusted with assignments involving some reasoning on the part of the animals. The Angus family, who lived in the Watson S.D. 1327 (Hamiota, Manitoba), owned a grey mare named Dolly that they used to transport their children to school. Everyone in the district spoke of Dolly as a wise old girl.

Indeed, she was just that! Before Leonard, the oldest boy, was big enough to hitch up the horse, the Angus children used to drive to school, turn Dolly around, tie up the lines, fasten them to the railing, and put the old dog in the driver's seat. The two returned home alone. As soon as the pair reached the Angus farmyard, someone came out to unharness the horse and put her in the warm barn. In the late afternoon, the process was reversed, and the faithful mare returned to school to pick up her passengers. The dog apparently went along

as an overseer, for if things did not suit his fancy, he barked incessantly or jumped out of the buggy and raced in front of the horse. Upon reaching the school, Dolly circled it once, stopped, and waited for the Angus children to clamber aboard. A couple of times during the year, Dolly figured she had waited long enough, and when the children did not appear promptly, she took off for home without them.

One day, Dolly missed the turnoff that led into the Angus farmyard and kept on going for a quarter of a mile down the main road. Like a human being, she had evidently become

This Shetland pony must have known that summers were supposed to be a holiday for him, too. The boys, Donald and Raymond Hoffman and Don McCandless, look quite happy, but the pony certainly doesn't!

Arthur and Marjorie Crisford drove Flossy and Glassie to Highland Park S.D. 2519 *(Sibbald, Alberta) in 1933.*

engrossed with her own problems and forgot to turn in at the proper place. Mr. Angus watched the proceedings with great interest. Once Dolly realized that she had gone too far, she stopped, considered her difficulty, backed the cutter off the road, taking care to keep herself neatly on the beaten ground, and after skillfully turning around, came back home.

Muriel (Griffiths) Bye still has a clipping from the front page of the March 3, 1939 edition of the Coronation *Review* that tells a remarkable story about her family and their school horses.

Polly and Jerry displayed lots of real horse sense! The team made two trips a day to school without a driver.

During cold weather, Mr. Griffiths was in the habit of driving his children to the Midvale S.D. 2413 (Coronation, Alberta), half a mile away in the morning with a team and sleigh and then returning for them again in the late afternoon. This additional assignment proved to be quite a chore as he already had work to do feeding and caring for a herd of stock during the short hours of daylight. One morning he complained to his wife, "I haven't time to drive the team to school today. I'm certain the boy can drive them, turn them around at school, and let them come home by themselves."

Mother was leary of this arrangement, but he managed to convince her that Polly and

Jerry would arrive home all right if the gate were left open. That afternoon, he decided to test his theory and sent the team back alone for the children. He hitched them to the sleigh, telling them repeatedly as he did so to go to school and fetch the children back. And that's just what they did! Although no one was around when they arrived at the school, as class was still in session, the team stopped as instructed and waited until school was dismissed. One can imagine the children's surprise to find the team waiting for them. From then on, Polly and Jerry saw to it that the children were driven to and from school daily—the perfect solution to their problem.

8 | The Sport of Kings

School horses did not just provide their owners with transportation; they did not merely fulfill the important task of delivering their children safely through all kinds of weather; nor did they exist merely to instruct their riders in the ways of the world. A school horse was indeed a very practical possession when one had four or five miles to travel twice a day, but he also provided recreation and entertainment for his master. School horses were fun, and to the children, that was their most important quality.

Perhaps it was a bit much to ask an old, worn-out school pony to pretend he was a prize three-year-old. But where else but in a horse race did a girl have such a good chance of beating a bragging boy? How could a boy be the Lone Ranger if he had no Silver? Without a horse, how could one practise important skills like circus stunts and trick riding?

Rodeos, Circuses, and Buffalo Hunts

Former students of one-room rural schools will attest to the fact that some school horses proved to be pretty fair rodeo stock. This was particularly true if sharp sticks, whips, hidden burrs, or meanness in general were brought into play in lieu of spurs. No matter how old Dobbin happened to be, under certain trying conditions thought up by his young master, he would buck, or at least rear up on his hind legs. Every now and then, when the teacher was out of the way, the students staged a stampede in the schoolyard, or if this was not possible, they settled for some convenient crossroad on the way home. These animals could be considered part of the school's unscheduled recreational program. (This type of activity must have some merit, for today centres like High River, De Winton, Coronation, and Sundre in Alberta sponsor Young Britches stampedes or rodeos exclusively for school children.)

One summer day in the Willowdale S.D. (Melfort, Saskatchewan), school traffic appeared congested in the vicinity of the barn, so Jennie, the teacher, went out to investigate. A pony circus was underway! One little fellow of about nine years of age excelled above all others. He was putting the teacher's quiet, good-natured old pony through a hectic pace to show off his skills as a cowboy. Old Pat

Albert Desilets was thrilled when he balanced himself successfully (and in heavy boots at that) on his horse's back at Corinth S.D. 2924 (Sunnynook, Alberta) in 1924.

A camera provided this boy with proof of his daredevil feats.

was visibly pleased when the teacher arrived and put a sudden stop to the exhibition. He neighed and extended his perspiring head to nuzzle her. A horse required a friend just as much as a human being in times of tribulation.

The school pony also had to be a polished actor or actress, as his or her young master was likely to star him in a variety of roles. A child mounted on a horse could easily imagine himself to be King Arthur, Joan of Arc, a crusader, or the Black Knight. The driver had only to find a discarded fence picket or break off a branch from a sapling and thus armed, gallop away on his charger to some battlefield or combat arena.

Irvin Roesler, who attended the Burnbrae S.D. (Compeer, Alberta), attributes the pains he still gets in his right shoulder to the lurch it received while jousting with a haystack some fifty years ago. Amazing, isn't it, how a pile of hay could bear even the faintest resemblance to a hideous fire-breathing monster? Yet to Irvin and to thousands of former pupils, their horses lent wings to their imaginations. In a flash, the knight's lance could become a rifle; the combatant himself, a proud Indian warrior; the steed, an Indian war pony; and the small clump of willows, a grazing buffalo ready to be slaughtered for food. In retrospect, Irvin philosophizes, "I am certain that if an Indian had been as ruthless a killer of buffalo as, in my imagination, I was, the buffalo would have been exterminated long before the arrival of the white man!"

Another important service rendered by the horse was the buildup to a boy's image when he described the feats of jumping, racing, or uncanny tricks performed by his animal the previous Saturday while out in the east pasture. Of course, these exploits could not be duplicated that particular day because the horse hadn't been given the necessary oats or simply didn't like to perform in front of a strange audience.

There's More than One Way to Ride a Buggy

The three Kowalski youngsters of the Vernon S.D. 3207 (Sibbald, Alberta) came up with a unique and dangerous way of driving a buggy to school. Some mornings, the trio came racing to school from the southeast, with the old buggy wheels rattling over the rocky road, the old horse straining and running his level best, while ten-year-old Emil (spread-legged and head bowed low) hung on for dear life to the spokes and rim of one of the hind wheels. He resembled a lobster as he clung to the wheel with his hands and feet. It took a tough, brave lad to perform such a dangerous feat, but Emil was equal to the task. During the stunt, Emil's equally fearless sisters did their best to bring out the best driving instincts the horse possessed.

Once Emil had an accident when the "operating" buggy wheel struck a large boulder on the road and propelled him off his perch on the wheel. He injured his head and went around with a bandage on it for several weeks. Emil did not do any "stunt driving" during this interval.

Many boys attempted to duplicate Emil's method of riding the hind wheel, but very few succeeded. It took someone with Emil's spirit to succeed at such a stunt. Throughout his career as a stunt man, Emil was brave, rash, inexpedient, and unbeatable, his motto: "If you don't succeed today, try it again tomorrow." There was no such thing as quitting; he kept on going until the project was a success.

Emil continued to persevere as a young man, exhibiting this trait while in the Canadian forces during World War II. He was killed while performing an act of courage, the kind he used to display while riding the hind wheels of that fast-moving buggy.

The children of Seven Persons S.D. 1440 (Seven Persons, Alberta) played an unusual game whenever there was a good strong wind

Kenneth Krogman and five other boys from the Bryant S.D. 2533 (Bindloss, Alberta) in *1929, having a great time hanging out in the buggies on the far side of the barn.*

blowing. It involved pulling a buggy to the far end of the schoolyard so the wind would blow it across to the other side. As many children as possible climbed into the buggy, pulled up the shafts, and held up a blanket as a sail. They were off on a wind-propelled ride across to the opposite fence. Then came the struggle against the force of the wind to return the vehicle for another joyride.

It's a Race!

The Little White Schoolhouse days were also the days of horse races. On those occasions, the homeward journey became an adventure. Unfortunately, now and then such races ended in misfortune.

Many pupils rode or drove to school, as evidenced by the large number of horses led from the barn when school was out. The kids, anxious to get home, passed their excitement on to the horses. There was also a lot of activity for a while in the schoolyard—it was always a contest to see who could get away from the yard first. More than once, several tried to go through the gate simultaneously, scraping the gate posts, and once in a while,

breaking them off. Usually, when the buggies turned onto the road, only two wheels would be on the ground.

On occasion, the older boys were permitted to drive a team of horses to school. This was the moment for which every rural youngster lived in anticipation. It was as much an achievement as attaining a driver's license today. The privilege of driving two horses showed that the lad had reached the age of discretion, and this in itself was enough to grant him some prestige in the eyes of his classmates. When two such outfits made their appearance in the same school, it was frequently a signal for some form of rivalry.

One such contest was to discover who could reach the school steps first, all hitched up and ready to start for home. Two boys, Ken and William, developed a keen competition until an accident put an end to their daily sport. On this particular day, Ken was forced to stay a few minutes after school in order to secure a homework assignment. For once, William had an advantage. Just as Ken was leading his team out of the barn, his competitor hooked up the last ring, jumped into the democrat, and brought his switch down on the rumps of his team. Off they went like a rocket! In circling the school steps, though, he swung too close; the two wheels on the right side went up over the stairs, throwing William out and turning the democrat completely upside down, its four wheels turning in the air. No one was more horrified than William's sisters, who were anxiously waiting on the platform above the steps. Miraculously, no one was injured!

An after-school horse race at the Stone Pile S.D. (Swift Current, Saskatchewan) in 1948.

Some horses experienced the joy of racing whenever they were out of sight of the teacher. There were horse races going, coming, and sometimes at noon. Everyone believed he or she had the best animal and was anxious to prove it. Could those ponies go! Fortunately, the jockeys clung like monkeys and became good riders, and seldom was anyone ever hurt.

Bill and Ann used to travel to the White Rose S.D. 365 (Windthorst, Saskatchewan) in a two-wheeled cart with no more space for their feet, schoolbags, lunch pails, and water pail than that provided by an apple box. In spite of its abbreviated appearance, the vehicle, like the chariots of old, proved to be just the right thing for racing. One contest

involving them and their neighbour's children was a memorable one.

Homeward bound, they raced neck and neck down the dusty road, followed by the other children, who were eager for some excitement. All too soon they reached the crossroads. When their neighbours made the quick turn to head homeward, Bill swerved his pony off the road to avoid a collision, only to catch a telephone pole squarely with one wheel. It was a sudden stop and a miracle that Bill and Ann crawled out alive—their two-wheeled cart had disintegrated as easily as if it had been made of matchsticks. The two youngsters, somewhat dazed, surveyed the results philosophically. They accepted an offer of a lift home. It wasn't until they were relating the incident to their parents that the full impact of their foolhardiness dawned on them.

A race in the Mountain Chase S.D. 1373 (Erickson, Manitoba) ended in a somewhat different manner. When one of the ponies was crowded, it dragged its youthful rider along a barbed-wire fence for some distance. The boy's right side, including his arm and leg, was so badly scraped that it resembled raw steak. Luckily, the scratches were superficial, and their gruesome appearance was worse than the actual damage. Experience was still not the best teacher, for the boy resumed racing after a short respite.

Girls were just as anxious as boys to challenge one another to a horse race. In the Raymond S.D. (Aneroid, Saskatchewan), Aileen vied with her girlfriend to see who could cover the first mile or so that they travelled together on the way home the fastest. Aileen's animal was part racehorse, so she invariably won the contest. She usually gave her opponent a sporting head start and then came roaring from behind to win the race by a nose. During one of those zestful competitions, the front wheel of Aileen's rig crossed over the rear axle of her friend's vehicle. The racing units became hopelessly interlocked. The animals seemed to comprehend the critical situation far better than their drivers, for they halted almost immediately and remained stationary. The two girls, after overcoming their initial fright, took out the buggy wrench and removed one of the wheels to free the two rigs.

Gladys and Randy Lundblad travelled to Longridge S.D. 837 (Holden, Alberta) in a two-wheeled chariot in the summertime. As in ancient Rome, it was indeed a superior racing machine.

This vehicle had tall wheels and long, protruding hubs. One day we coaxed Helen Grinde into racing with us. Posthaste, Helen sent her team and Bennett buggy hurtling down the road with us in hot pursuit! Most of the pupils were beside themselves when they saw this thundering chaos coming down the public highway. As we passed Helen, our hub accidently came too close to her buggy's front wheel, and her spokes were transformed into kindling. Ah, those were the days!

In the Turtle S.D. (Trochu, Alberta) between 1911 and 1922, it was races between the Anderson boys and Johnson girls in their respective sleighs that caused all the excitement.

Shorty usually took the lead, passed everyone, and while turning the corner, tipped the sleigh, spilling us kids. Shorty then raced home, sometimes with the sleigh attached and at other times, with just the pull-shafts behind. As no one got hurt, it was fun for us, but not for Father Hanna. He had to rebuild the Eaton Company's original. Mr. Hanna's workmanship outlasted the Eaton Company's for many years.

The Georgetown S.D. 3232 (Delia, Alberta) was built near a deep, steep-sided coulee. When the school first opened in May of 1921, only three pupils came from the west. Mike and Bert Marshall rode a stiff-legged horse named Ginger, while Johnny made the trip astride a small sorrel mare.

To reach the school gate, the boys rode down the west side of the coulee across a wooden bridge, up the other side, round a curve, and finally turned sharply into the entrance of the schoolyard.

One morning, Mike challenged Johnny to a race to the schoolyard. Mike won, but as he navigated the turn at the gate entrance, the saddle slipped, and he fell off. Bert, however, had wound the straps which hung from the sides of the saddle round and round his hands

and was unable to let go. His feet were caught in the stirrups. Poor Bert hung like a burr to the fastenings, yelling at Mike, who stood nearby laughing as hard as the rest of the pupils. He did manage to say, "He's swearing in Italiano," which all of us understood. Ginger just stood there, motionless! Finally, one of the older girls went to Bert's aid, helping him free his hands and disengage his feet.

The children spent several days thanking faithful old Ginger for stopping so suddenly and remaining still, for it was she who was responsible for preventing injury to Bert.

To the children of the Clover Bar S.D. 212 (Edmonton, Alberta), Empire Day in 1931 meant flags, a gift from the teacher, and a ride home on either a school horse or, increasingly, a bicycle.

Skipper Was Second, but not with Me!

Skipper was fifteen and Darrel Suddably, eight when the two became daily travelling companions on the road to Rosegarland S.D. 2009 (Viking, Alberta). Skipper was experienced; Darrel was not.

Her name was Skipper. She was about fourteen hands high, slightly sway-backed, dark brown with a white face, and marked with a light spot low on her right side directly behind her front leg. Her ancestry is unknown, except that she had some Shetland blood, which probably contributed to her longevity.

Dad bought Skipper from his cousin Reginald Suddably. Skipper had been his wife Margaret's school pony and had taken her to Pleasant Ridge S.D. 3065 (Lavoy, Alberta) for several years.

That horse carried me everywhere I wanted to go, mainly to school and back but also to my grandparents' farm, to round up the cows, and to visit my friends. My brothers, sisters, and I learned most of what we know about riding horses from her. We became adept at falling off and, in fact, learned how to do this while holding on to the reins, a necessary skill since she was in the habit of shying often and quickly and did not always wait patiently for her victims to remount.

When we took over Skipper, she was still a fast horse—not quite as fast as Rex, the part-thoroughbred that Glen Simmonds rode, but faster than Cecil Simmonds's pony, Goldie. In the impromptu races our parents warned us not to conduct but did anyway, we finished in the following order: Rex, then Skipper, and finally, Goldie; all other participants were left in the dust. This perilous combination of horse racing and Skipper's shying led to the roughest landing I ever experienced.

One fall day, Mom and Dad drove a team and wagon over to visit a neighbour who lived south of Rosegarland. Our farm was located northwest of the school, and they happened to be en route home when school was dismissed. As we were leaving the schoolyard, Glen unlatched the big metal gate, rode Rex through, and released it. Cecil took Goldie through without mishap, but by the time Skipper and I reached the opening, the gate had swung back far enough to force my animal to crowd the gatepost to get through. As we went through the gate, a piece of wire tore my pants and opened a gash in my right knee.

Now, cleaved pants and a cut knee don't stop a nine-year-old boy when there is a chance to race, and since we had the excuse of trying to catch Mom and Dad's wagon, away we went! Suddenly, Skipper shied at some cattle in the trees beside the road. Since I was riding bareback and leaning well up on her neck, there was no possibility of staying aboard the animal, so I went, face first, onto the dirt road! With a skinned face, a gashed knee, and my insides aching, I swore I'd never ride horseback again. They loaded me into the wagon, took me home, and put me to bed. An hour later, when the pain had subsided, I went back to Skipper and fetched the cattle.

During the first three years we owned Skipper, we lived about two and a half miles from Rosegarland School, but in the spring, we moved to a farm only half a mile away. I continued riding Skipper in spite of the short distance I needed to cover. I had one problem, however: Skipper was difficult to catch when turned loose. She could empty the oat bucket used to entice her without allowing herself to be caught. The most successful method of catching her was to trap her in a fenced corner. Since we turned our horses loose to graze in the schoolyard while we attended classes, I spent many afternoons running one or two miles trying to corner and catch Skipper so I could ride the half-mile home.

Skipper permitted a young man's imagination to wander, and she assumed whatever role was required to support it. I could be Roy Rogers; she'd be Trigger. I'd be Gene Autry; she'd be Champion. Being the wrong colour or sex didn't matter. When her rider pretended to be a jockey, she would race around a grove of trees in the pasture or whatever else

was chosen to be the track. She would canter as a jumping horse and leap over logs and ditches or be a bulldogging horse if her rider decided to agitate the head of a milch cow. Her rider could even pretend to be a world champion broncobuster, digging his heels into her flanks till she bucked. We competed in the show classes at the Vegreville Exhibition on many occasions, but somehow the judges never chose "Trigger" as the best horse in "his" class, as I did. No ribbons ever came her way!

The worst experience Skipper and I had occurred in the summer of 1949. Carl Rock and I were riding from the hamlet of Ranfurly, Alberta, to the Rock farm when we came face to face with a skunk! Carl held up for a second and then quickly urged his horse by. I tried the same stunt, but as I passed the skunk, he sprayed Skipper right behind the saddle. I managed to ride her the remaining mile to the Rock's, then quickly turned her out to the pasture. The poor pony didn't have any company, by way of people or other horses, near her for a solid week.

Skipper lived to be thirty-nine years of age. When I was promoted to riding larger horses, my brothers and sisters took over riding her to Rosegarland School and used her for getting the cows. Eventually my siblings and I moved from the farm, leaving Skipper to take life pleasantly. In her last years, she grazed with the cattle in summer, and Dad fed her with them in the winter. Occasionally, one of us would take her for a short ride when visiting the farm. Later, there were grandchildren to ride her. Skipper performed well

In 1930, some students at Devonshire S.D. (Youngstown, Alberta) were anxious to show off their artwork. Others, however, like the two boys in the Lone Ranger masks on their school horse's back, exhibited their imaginations in other ways.

in all these old-timers' activities. The last time I rode her, she was well into her thirties. I slid back, touched her flanks, and she bucked.

Now, almost forty years after Skipper became my school pony, I still own and enjoy riding horses. The sense of pleasure derived from horseback riding goes back to my boyhood and the time I spent with Skipper. If there is a heaven for school ponies, she must be there, front and centre.

9 | Winter

Winter created additional hardships for the children and their beasts of burden. As trails and roads were often obliterated by drifting snow, the young drivers had to develop a keen sense of direction in order to be able to reach home and school safely. Then, there were always blizzards to be confronted. With very few roads, fences, or other landmarks to use as guides, it was easy to get lost in the blinding snow.

Despite the fact that windchill temperatures were unheard of in those days, they were most certainly felt. A rural child considered himself fortunate indeed to survive a winter without having his nose, cheeks, fingers, or toes frozen at least once. Chilblains is only a word in the dictionary today, but practically every adult who once attended a rural school can recall the excruciating pain and inflammatory sores produced by overexposure of hands and feet to the bitter cold. The most distressing moment was when the toes and fingers started to thaw out. Every morning in the classroom, a child would be bitterly crying from recurrent chilblains.

Combating the Cold

There were various ways of combating the cold. The simplest method was to wrap preheated rocks in gunny sacks or old newspapers and place them on the floor of the cutter or sleigh. The heat radiating from these footwarmers kept the children reasonably warm. It was a winter morning ritual to fish the hot stones out of the kitchen range and gingerly carry them out to the waiting school vehicle. Once in the cutter, the children enveloped themselves in heavy horse blankets and buffalo robes. No rural child could ever forget the characteristic odour of the singed horse blankets that usually lay near the hot rocks. The combined effect of the footwarmer, the weighty clothes, and the vast array of covers often made it too warm for the passengers. Hence, at times it was necessary for them to break out of their cocoon-like wrappings to avoid the nausea brought on by the lack of fresh air and the stifling heat.

Another gimmick that worked exceedingly well was a canvas or wooden caboose built on the sleigh. This arrangement provided good shelter for the children. In addition, if a small heater were installed inside, it became possible for passengers to travel for many miles without feeling the effects of the wind or cold.

Those who travelled on horseback were not as fortunate. No matter how warmly they dressed, their vulnerable position on the horse made them easy prey to the biting cold. They usually rode bareback because they had learned from experience that a soft, furry hide was much warmer than a cold, hard saddle. At first glance, they resembled a small army of pudgy robots riding into the schoolyard. The many clothes they wore distorted their shapes, and the hoarfrost-covered scarves that swathed their heads endowed them with grotesque visages. These equestrians were so stiff from their long rides and the cold that they dismounted with slow precision, as if mechanically controlled. The machine-like illusion disappeared in a flash the moment the riders began to warm their hands between the legs of their horses.

Three pupils from the Balmoral S.D. 292 (Red Deer, Alberta) were heading home on a bitterly cold winter day, with two youngsters in a sleigh and the other on a saddle horse. The lad on horseback was complaining loudly about how cold the weather was and how cold he was. When asked why he didn't get off and walk to keep himself warm, he stubbornly replied, "I'd rather freeze to death like a man than run like a dog."

Nothing chilled the hands of a school horseman to the bone more than when he had to hold on to something like a parcel, lunch pail, books, or just the reins during even a short trip in intensely cold weather. Andy Marshall once froze his hands while carrying a cake to school. The occasion was the first school party held in the Georgetown S.D. (Delia, Alberta) during the winter of 1912. The three Marshall brothers rode together on horseback to attend the festivities. Andy had been assigned the task of taking care of the

cake. He succeeded in getting it to school intact but had become so engrossed in the importance of his mission that he neglected to wriggle his fingers inside his mitts to maintain circulation. Both Andy's hands were badly frostbitten by the time the trio had covered the two and a half miles to the Georgetown School. Everybody at the party enjoyed the novelty of having a cake at school except the lad responsible for getting it there. He suffered too greatly from chilblains to enjoy anything.

Winters were hard on horses, too. The snowy roads made travel difficult for them, food was scarce, and the stables, cold. Where

Transportation to Summerhill S.D. (Endiang, Alberta) in the winter of 1933: horse, *homemade skis, and sleigh.*

stables were nonexistent, the poor beasts were forced to stand outside all day tied to a hitching post, sleigh, or fence post.

From 1911 to 1922, Lillian (Ranta) Burch enjoyed her trips to the Turtle S.D. (Trochu, Alberta) a great deal more than the horse that pulled her.

The Hanna kids came in a sleigh in the winter, and I always managed to get a ride with them. Arvo Ranta and Matt Hanna wore skis and hung on to the sleigh, one person on each side. The rest of us piled into the body of the sleigh, while Ike acted as teamster. In the mornings the horse, Shorty, was steady and quiet, though he always reached school on time; but when home-time came, the horse, after standing in the cold barn all day, became very spirited. Poor Ike wrestled vigorously to try to hold the horse back. Ike was just a slight little guy then and had to brace his feet against the dashboard. Fairly frequently, Shorty spilled us out of the bobsled before we left the schoolyard.

Anyone who has had the misfortune to touch a piece of metal on a cold day will appreciate the discomfort and pain experienced by a horse when a cold steel bit is quickly thrust into his mouth on a winter day. Most school barns were not too warm, so by dismissal time, the bits were icy cold. Some considerate children warmed the piece of metal against their own bodies before inserting it into the pony's mouth. Others simply forced the cold steel bar between the animal's lips and teeth without any pangs of remorse.

The students in the Marmer S.D. 415 (Somerset, Manitoba) must have belonged to the humanitarian society. They were in the habit of smuggling the bridles into the school during afternoon recess and concealing them under their coats, which hung on the wall beside the heater. By dismissal time, the bits were as warm as toast and ready for instant use. The aroma of leather assailed the nostrils of the teacher, but being of a kind nature, she ignored what her trained eye had not missed.

A Blizzard Caught Us

When blizzards swept across the open countryside, there were no phones, no radios, no daily newspapers, and no television sets to issue storm warnings in those early pioneer days.

The absence of any reliable communication between the school and the various homes during a blizzard was a source of much torment for the teacher, the children, and the parents. Only those who have been through such an experience can appreciate what it is like to be isolated by a severe storm with no means whatsoever of making contact with the outside world.

The morning of January 23, 1934, dawned cold and grey as Elsie (Coad) Rogers prepared lunches for her three older children: Eldon, ten; Ethel, eleven; and Eileen, fourteen. In the meantime, the youngsters were bundling up in their warmest clothes, and their dad was harnessing and hitching Nibs to the toboggan. Though they thought nothing of it at the time, the calmness of this dull, overcast day might have signalled an impending storm, but the fierceness of the ensuing blizzard could not have been foreseen.

Their vehicle was a large toboggan that George Rogers had fashioned from a binder

table. The front part was rolled up and tied back to a two-by-six-inch frame fastened to the outside edge of the metal. This provided a low enclosure that they filled with straw and in which the kids huddled against the cold and the snow flying from the horse's hooves.

On this particular morning, five-year-old Allen followed Ethel around the kitchen with a single match and prattled, "Here, Tid," his name for her at the time, "you take this!" And without attaching any particular significance to the act, she pocketed the match.

Their route to the Farming Valley S.D. 2796 (Cereal, Alberta), three and a half miles

These Clairmont, Alberta, children went to school in toboggans pulled by their school horses in the winter of 1935.

away, was through open pasture land for a good part of the way. Misfortune overtook them about a mile from home when the toboggan caught on a snow-covered rock and flipped them upside down. Eileen and Ethel tumbled clear, but Eldon turned up underneath a pile of straw, blankets, books, and lunches. The two girls worked hastily to extricate their brother, right the toboggan, reload all the essentials, and get ready to move on again.

Just at that moment, the wind rose sharply, the day darkened, and driving snow filled the air. A furious blizzard had reached them, with its swirling and stinging snow. They could barely see the horse's head. In fact, it seemed as if they were engulfed on all sides, as well as above and below, in howling whiteness. They continued on their way, however, until Nibs stopped and refused to go further. The girls investigated and discovered their horse was leaning over an old fence—one that they could not identify as no fences existed along the first two miles of their route to school. They were quite cold by now, and after a few minutes of shivering and discussing their predicament, they agreed to follow the fence to the left. Having lost all sense of direction by this time, they weren't sure in which direction they would be headed by going left, but thought it was probably either south or east.

Eventually they reached a niche in the fence with a rock pile. After a very heated and almost hysterical debate (for they were extremely cold, and the girls' legs and faces were frozen in patches), they finally identified the corner and straightened out their direc-

tions. They were three-quarters of a mile south of the Garnett Morris farmhouse, which they decided to head for rather than attempt to find the school, even though there was no fence to follow northward.

They hadn't gone more than a few yards from the corner before they found themselves lost again. Even the road and corner they had just left were next to impossible to find. After wandering back and forth, they eventually found the corner again. This time, instead of following the road, they decided to walk directly along the line of telephone poles. The poles no longer had wires on them, and they soon discovered that when they were between poles, they could see neither the one behind nor the one ahead. Frequently, they became lost for brief periods of time in trying to make just one hundred feet of headway. Even by returning to the pole they had just passed, they were unable to determine in which direction they should proceed to the next one as there were no markers to go by and the storm continued to rage so furiously that it seemed to come from all sides at once. They solved this dilemma, to a degree, by having one of them walk ahead of the horse, another in back of the toboggan, and shouting back and forth; they could thus get from pole to pole.

Finally, they caught sight of the Morris's caragana hedge beside the road. It appeared eery and unnatural in the gloom of the storm, and they weren't certain that they had actually reached the Morris place. They plunged through the deep snow, led Nibs right up onto the verandah, and rushed into the house.

The Spinks and Kingcott children co-operated to get to school in the winter of 1935, each family contributing a horse (Tom and Roanie) *to make up the needed team. They kept warm by bundling up and stuffing six bodies into a small homemade cutter.*

The girls' legs were badly frostbitten, and all had icy patches on their faces. Eileen and Ethel ran round and round in the house, stamping their feet and crying in pain. With the exception of his face and fingers, Eldon appeared to be in good shape, so he tried to stop his sisters long enough to rub snow on their frozen legs. Soon they were assisting each other with this treatment, and Eldon began looking around the house for paper, wood, and other combustible material with which to start a fire in the old stove that still remained in the kitchen.

When all was in readiness, the three children, very conscious of the sole match in their possession, gathered around the paper and the shavings Eldon had made with his jackknife. Fortunately, the match flamed into life perfectly, and in a few minutes, there was a fire in the resurrected stove. Unfortunately, the stove pipes had been removed, and the flames and smoke belched two or three feet from the chimney opening in the stove, driving the children away. It was a wonder they didn't burn down the house. Something had to be done and done quickly!

There were numerous jam, lard, and tobacco cans scattered about the house, so Eldon, using his jackknife, began carving the bottoms out of them and fitting the resulting cylinders together to form a serviceable stove pipe. In the end he had constructed some six feet of pipe, enough to reach from the stove to a ceiling outlet. These glowed cherry red near the stove, and gradually the smoke cleared, enabling the children to approach the stove and enjoy its warmth. They collected a large pile of wood, wrenching pieces from the railings and floor of the verandah, now conveniently fragmented to a considerable extent due to Nibs's weight.

In time, they were cozily warm, enjoying waiting out the storm, and hopefully anticipating their lunches, which were thawing out near the stove. Ethel and Eldon took pity on the poor horse and decided to settle her down in the barn.

Several partridges had taken refuge from the storm in the barn, so for the moment, Nibs was forgotten while the children, armed with sticks, chased the birds back and forth, finally killing three of them. Then they tended to Nibs, covered her with blankets, gave her the bag of oats that was her usual noonday meal, and proceeded triumphantly back to the house with the three birds.

They scalded the partridges in boiling snow-water, plucked and cleaned them, and returned them to boil in the melted snow. The birds made an extremely tasty meal that afternoon. No heads of state dined with greater enthusiasm and sheer joy than our trio of scholars on that terrible day.

Later that afternoon, the blizzard began to subside, and the wind howled less loudly. The children kept a roaring fire going and were snug, cozy, and even drowsing on the floor. Later, they gathered a large pile of wood from wherever they could tear it off the house in preparation for the coming night. They read some of their school books, told stories, and laughed about how uncomfortable they had been that morning. At times, they thought about their mom and dad, who, they were sure, would be wondering why they hadn't returned home from school at the usual time.

Little did the youngsters realize the consternation they created in the district that day. When Mr. Rogers called at the Farming Valley School at 3:30 to pick up his children, the teacher, Mrs. C. Lodmell, had to say, "But your children weren't at school today!" Never in her life had she harder words to say! Several search parties, hastily organized, combed the prairie for the trio.

Around five o'clock, the children heard shouts and the tinkle of sleigh bells, and when they looked out the door, they saw the lights of coal-oil lanterns approaching. It turned out to be George Rogers and Joe Vanstone. They were extremely surprised and relieved to find the children, having given up hope of ever seeing them alive again. It was an emotional scene, but poor Eldon, after all his labours at more or less methodically destroying the house while ensuring their welfare for the coming night, was fleetingly furious at having been found!

The entire group returned home in Joe Vanstone's warm sleigh, complete with foot-warmers and many blankets, for a joyful reunion with their distraught mother, who had been sick with worry all day, not having seen or heard anything of the children since morning, nor of their dad, who had left home early that afternoon to fetch them from school.

Sometimes the youngsters got "caught out" if a blizzard blew in while they were in school. A surprising variety of vehicles would quickly appear at the school door: possibly a stoneboat loaded with blankets, a home-made cutter with the snow-covered horses dancing in a fever to get home again, or it might be a bobsled with an accumulation of lean-wheat straw in the bottom in which to snuggle, or a cutter pulled by a fast Shetland pony. The shivering horses patiently waited while the children struggled to do up their four-buckled, black cloth overshoes. The youngsters crammed a few books into the sugar-sack schoolbags, grabbed the syrup-pail lunch buckets, and away they would jingle home through the howling blizzard.

A Free Rein

The horse, with his uncanny sense of direction, if given a free rein, brought the kids safely home time after time through severe snow storms.

Walter Lutz and his sisters, Gertie and Alice, drove Mary, a black, part-Percheron mare, to West Bruce S.D. (Bruce, Alberta) in the 1940s. The children had been told to put their trust in Mary; one day that trust was put to the test.

In early March of 1948, a sudden winter storm struck our area shortly after dinner with strong winds, driving snow, and falling temperatures. The teacher hurriedly dismissed school, sending the children scurrying for home.

As we began the journey home, visibility was virtually zero, and the windchill, extremely high. Dad always told us, if we couldn't see in a storm, to "Just let Mary find her way home, and don't try to drive."

I recall huddling under the blanket in the cutter while my oldest sister held the lines. We couldn't see a thing, so we let Mary find her way home. It seemed like an eternity before Mary stopped—right outside the barn door! I wonder: was she only thinking of her warm stall, the feed box of oats, and the green feed in the manger? Or was it some sense of duty and loyalty that made her bring four very frightened and very cold children home to a thankful, crying mother and a grateful father? I know for a fact that Mary received an extra portion of oats and hay that evening.

School horses were also trusted to prevent their masters from doing anything foolhardy. School horses did what they had to do, but they were smart enough to know what really could not be done. Hazel (Swalm) Cahoon, who attended Merrington S.D. 2604 near Kindersley, Saskatchewan, will never forget

Students in the Rush Centre S.D. 2769 (Oyen, Alberta), going home in homemade covered *sleighs during the Depression—there was no money to buy factory-made cutters.*

the intelligence of the Lynch family's pair of thoroughbreds.

Tom Lynch's son, Keith, and daughter, Joan, rode thoroughbreds, using English saddles. I was astonished at the speed they could muster up. Our horses were of the large, workhorse type, so I had to be satisfied with a slow, cloppy-clop jog! The Lynch horses could be driven, too.

I recall one Christmas concert night in the poor thirties. A blizzard blew in with such force and snow as to cut down visibility to nil.

The Lynch family set out with horses and cutter for the school, and eventually found that the equines took them back home. They set out twice more, and again the animals brought them home. Finally, Mr. Lynch telephoned the school to explain the situation. I've often thought how smart those horses were! Keith Lynch had a very important role to play in the three-act Christmas play, so this was quite a letdown to all, particularly his teacher, who dressed up as a man and filled in for her pupil.

Keeping School Overnight

The majority of rural teachers were familiar with the unwritten law that if a blizzard struck during school hours, the children were to remain inside the school and not be dismissed until someone came for them. Nevertheless, once in a while some willful or anxious youngster defied the precept and ventured into the storm alone.

One January afternoon in the year 1916, Sadie Robinson, the teacher in the Orange View S.D. (Watrous, Saskatchewan), noticed that as the time drew near for the last recess, the classroom was growing darker. She opened the porch door and discovered that it was snowing heavily, although it was still fairly mild and calm. By 3:30, the wind had increased in velocity and visibility was reduced considerably. There was no doubt about it, the Orange View School was in the path of a howling blizzard. Miss Robinson immediately recalled school and instructed the boys and girls not to venture outside the building, not even to the barn or outhouses.

It simply wasn't safe! The children, being more aware of the dangers of going out into a blizzard than Miss Robinson (who had recently arrived from Ontario), agreed forthwith to remain indoors.

No one came to take the children home. After eating the remains of their noon lunches, the students participated in a variety of activities organized by the teacher. They played games, sang songs, acted out plays, and told stories. Soon the lamps were lit and the furnace filled with coal, so at least they had light and heat. No one complained, although food was mentioned many times in their comments to each other. The storm appeared to worsen, although during brief lulls, the clouds parted to reveal a full moon.

It was during one of these brief periods that the oldest boy was tempted to disobey orders. He slipped out unseen and started, on foot, for his home. The lad had gone just a few rods past the school gates when he completely lost his bearings. The storm once again closed in. In the process of turning around to shield his face from the onslaught of the snow, he spied a faint glow. He was certain that it came from one of the windows of the schoolhouse. The youth managed to struggle back to safety. Just as the teacher and other students noticed his absence from the group, the door blew open and in he stumbled, covered in snow from head to toe. They had difficulty identifying the snowman. Had it not been for the light, the boy swore he never would have found his way back. How thankful they all were for that coal-oil lamp!

The children and teacher now realized it was hopeless to expect anyone to come for them that evening, so they prepared for sleep. Using coats and wraps over the seats and desks, beds were improvised for the little ones. The older boys decided to roost on the top beam of the three-quarter-height partition that separated the cloakroom from the classroom. Miss Robinson and the girls just rested and talked. They often stopped their chatting to listen to the weird sounds made by the wind as it called down the chimney, or they watched at the windows as the snow swirled outside the school. The hours dragged on interminably to the accompaniment of the clamorous blizzard. Often, smaller children awakened, calling, "Mama! Mama!" and then dropped back to sleep, whimpering fitfully into their makeshift pillows.

At about 2:30 in the morning, the storm abated somewhat, and the sleepy youngsters were aroused by the arrival of a couple of anxious fathers who had brought hot coffee and sandwiches for the pupils. What a never-to-be-forgotten party it turned out to be! The men, seeing that the boys and girls were safe and comfortable, decided to leave them at school for the rest of the night. They

The Lutz boys, off to Bachelor S.D. 5009 in a heated van.

themselves returned home! Once again the room grew quiet as the youngsters settled back to sleep.

At daybreak, the shrill crowings of the "roosters" perched upon the beam roused everyone from sleep. Soon, worried parents began arriving. They had braved the storm to come and get their children. For a week after that winter ordeal, the school at Orange View remained closed.

Stanley Johnson, a teacher in the Roselea S.D. (Readlyn, Saskatchewan), experienced "keeping school" overnight during a blizzard in the winter of 1943.

Instead of the storm subsiding, as it usually did as the afternoon wore on, the wind increased in tempo and blew into a real blizzard. By three o'clock he was receiving telephone messages from parents who wanted their children kept at school, rather than having them venture out into the storm. He assured the parents that all the students would remain overnight at the school and that everything was under control.

The barn was less than a hundred feet away from the schoolhouse, but it was not visible in the windswept snow. Nevertheless, the teacher and a couple of the bigger boys braved the storm to reach it and find out how the five horses were faring. They were fine! The boys plugged the worst cracks in the barn with straw, threw the animals some snow to quench their thirst, and headed back to school. They brought with them a good supply of coal and wood as well as all the blankets that had been left in the cutters. The latter, which they planned to use as bedding, were shaken and spread to dry near the stove.

It didn't take long for the children to arrange an impromptu concert to amuse themselves until supper was ready. The teacherage was a lean-to in back of the schoolhouse, so with kitchen facilities close at hand, it wasn't difficult to prepare a meal. Unfortunately, the teacher's supply of food was low, hence supper consisted primarily of oatmeal porridge and dried fruit.

After eating, the youngsters pushed the desks to the sides of the room and started a dance party. One girl was a better-than-average pianist, so they enjoyed a lively time. The blizzard, whipping around the corners of the school, was completely forgotten in the excitement of performing various square dances and schottisches.

Mr. Johnson signalled bedtime at ten o'clock. The five girls retired to the teacherage, where they all slept together in one small bed. How they managed this feat, the teacher never learned. In the meantime, the four boys and the teacher arranged a few long benches side by side to improvise beds for themselves, and all available coats were employed as substitutes for blankets. They fixed up the fire and retired for the night.

Morning found nine hungry students. Whatever remained in Mr. Johnson's larder was consumed for breakfast, but it was still not enough. He appeased their appetites with pancakes of his own devising. School carried on as usual following breakfast but with many nodding heads. Later that morning, the blizzard subsided, and food (for both the humans and the horses) was brought to the school. Soon everyone, except the teacher, was bound for home and a good night's rest.

All They Could Do Was Wait

Parents, waiting for their children to return from school when a blizzard blew in near dismissal time, knew what an agonizing interim it was. From experience, they knew that large drifts formed rapidly on the unfenced fields so that horses floundered, stumbled, and plunged to break through, often losing their way on the prairie. Fathers and mothers watched as the clouds thickened, the savage blizzard growing fiercer and fiercer, and felt the cold intensifying. They listened as the storm raged and roared around the corners of the house, wondering all the while whether their children were still at school or somewhere out in the storm. Mothers scratched peepholes in the frosted windowpanes, watching and waiting for a familiar horse and cutter to loom into view, but saw nothing more than the whirling veil of whiteness.

As if in answer to her wishes, her husband occasionally shuffled outside to assess the situation. These little forays into the edge of the blizzard rarely brought encouragement. "I think it's getting worse!" he would often report. The storm lent credence to his statement by buffeting the house and rattling the windows with a few extra-powerful gusts. There was little parents could do except pace the floor nervously and hope.

Occasionally, the father would uneasily gather together his heavy clothes, placing them beside the oven in anticipation of the journey to school should the children fail to show up soon. Then all at once, above the roar of the storm, the parents simultaneously heard the joyous crunch, crunch of the horse's hooves and the creak of the runners

Bessie and Leslie Watkins, ready for a frosty trip to Rye S.D. in the winter of 1929.

in the snow. Almost instantly the noisy young-sters burst into the house, eager to tell of their trip, and once more happiness reigned in the household.

Blizzards are so unpredictable that, despite the many gains that have been made in the science of weather forecasting in recent years, it is still difficult to foretell with any degree of certainty when or where a blizzard may oc-cur or its intensity. One rural district may be enjoying a balmy afternoon, while another, not too many miles removed from the first, may be isolated completely by a severe storm. In the days of the Little White Schoolhouse, parents often relied on their own scientific methods to determine whether or not it was safe for their children to start for school.

Irvin Roesler, who attended the Burnbrae S.D. (Compeer, Alberta) between 1945 and 1949, recalls the method his parents used to ascertain whether it was safe enough for him to start out on the two-and-a-half-mile journey to school.

A railroad ran through our property, less than a quarter of a mile from the barn, and if the storm was severe enough to obliterate the snow fence along the Canadian Pacific Railway right-of-way, I was given a holiday. More than once, I was able to wrangle a day off by resorting to fraudulent methods. I can remember watching the snow fence as much as possible during the morning chores, and whenever a strong gust of wind came up and whirled the snow about to such an extent as to blur the outline of the fence, I immediately called my father's attention to it. As a result of my keen sense of observation, I received more unscheduled holidays than was really necessary.

In all fairness to Irvin Roesler, the snow fence visibility criterion was quite unreliable, so at times, he rode through severe blizzards to reach home after school was dismissed.

On one such occasion, the chin strap on the hood of his heavy parka came undone while he was still three-quarters of a mile from home. Irvin stopped the horse, turned him around to face away from the raw wind, and tried to fasten the dangling cords. His attempts proved fruitless. The cold was so intense that, having removed his mittens to get at the drawstrings, his hands numbed from the cold so quickly that he could not perform the delicate task of tying a knot. After a few useless attempts, Irvin gave up and decided to make a mad dash for home. He was aware of the biting frost on his face and chin during the fast ride but did not realize until he entered the warm confines of the kitchen that his cheeks and chin were frozen. His cheeks responded to a brisk rubbing with snow, but his chin wept and peeled for days afterwards. Unlike the children of today, rural youngsters in those days did not have to be coaxed to dress warmly. They knew from experience the hazards of wearing insufficient clothing.

The Christmas Concert

Shirlee (Smith) Matheson remembers the prairie winter as more than just endless bone-chilling rides to school. There were snowball fights and sleigh rides, but best of all, there was the Christmas concert. Each December, everyone crowded into the little one-room schoolhouse to watch the programme the children and their teacher had prepared and wait for Santa Claus. Santa, of course, arrived in a sleigh, but reindeer didn't pull it—like everyone else in those days, Santa's sleigh was pulled by horses!

How well I remember the winter of '48. It was my first year in a one-room country school. I was the lone outsider, the only non-Ukrainian girl in the valley.

The Christmas concert, followed by a supper and dance, was the focal point of the winter's entertainment. The night of the concert, I stood impatiently by our kitchen door, almost immobilized in my woollen coat and hat, knitted scarf, two pairs of mitts, wool stockings, leggings, and heavy felt boots, waiting while Mother made her painstaking rounds, checking the stove, blowing out the coal-oil lamp. At last she announced we would go.

"Come on! Come on!" she said, in her Scottish accent, "We'll be late."

I turned and trudged heavily out to the waiting cutter. Our black mare tossed her head back and forth, getting used to the stiff, cold bridle and bit. The black leather harness, adorned with silver studs, gleamed and danced in the moonlight.

My brother and I settled down on the little seat at the front of the cutter, facing our parents on the main bench seat, and pulled the buffalo robe up around our chins. With a flick of the leather lines, which passed between my brother's head and mine, the horse lunged forward. The sleigh runners loosened suddenly from their bed of soft snow, and we glided past the smooth frozen river, past the hunched cows standing in hoary groups under their snow blankets, and down to the main gate.

As my father jumped out to open the wire gate, we could hear the jingle of an approaching sleigh, that of our neighbour, Pete Kuzenko and his family. They rode stylishly in a van (a sleigh resembling a modern camper), complete with a coal-burning heater, drawn by two big black horses. We waved and called out, our "Merry Christmas!" greetings spangling through the still night air.

Our horse turned now onto the main road. Her hooves beat out muted base-notes on the hard packed snow, every few steps releasing a piece of packed snow that threw back scents

The Droneck's school horse, Frank, was ready to take all four Droneck children to Cavell S.D. (Preeceville, Saskatchewan) both winter and summer. The summer transportation system, a buggy, had been abandoned in favour of a cutter because of the deep snow.

of barn, soft straw, and old manure. I sat back and looked up at the stars, trying to find the Hunter and the Big Dipper. The glow of the moon reflected off the banks of snow at the sides of the road, turning them into heaped treasure.

The schoolyard was already filled with sleighs abandoned at reckless angles. We worked our way out from the tangles of heavy buffalo robe and gingerly jumped down, our legs stiff from their cramped position. Dad took the horses to the barn while my mother, brother, and I entered the schoolhouse.

The small entry porch had become a tunnel, closed in from each side by layer upon layer of coats, hats, and scarves that grew out from the hooks. The floor was a carpet of black rubber galoshes. Adding ours, we stumbled through the clutter and became, at once, part of the festivities that changed our staid chalky-smelling school into a temple of magic. I edged around the piano and entered the world of the stage, an area sectioned off by a curtain made from white sheets and dark red bedspreads. Behind the stage set, two big grade fours were crying; pieces of their costumes had been lost. Pale and stricken grade twos had forgotten their parts. The girl who was to play Mary was sick. Everyone had the sudden urge to go to the bathroom, a frozen shack fifty feet from the school; most tried to hold it, some with no success. I found the grade ones crowded into a corner. We had the opening number: Each in turn to hold up a letter spelling out "MERRY CHRISTMAS" and recite a line to set it off. "C is for the Christ child" was my responsibility.

We peeked through a small hole in the sheet and watched the school fill up. Mothers, aunts, older sisters, and a few men occupied the board benches, while the fathers and young men stood importantly at the back, forming the stag line. Children not taking part in the concert were asked to sit quietly on the floor at the front, where papers had been laid to keep their good clothes from being soiled by the oiled floors.

Suddenly, a hush fell over the audience! Our teacher was at the front of the stage, large and significant in her bright coral-coloured dress set off by a sparkling rhinestone brooch.

"Good evening," she began in English, then, *"Dobryi vechir,"* for in our valley there were many who could not speak much English.

"Dobryi vechir!" the audience roared back.

"Now," Mrs. Leschuk continued in her teacher voice, "let's all stand for 'O Canada'!"

She clumped down the two plank steps and sounded out the introductory chords on the piano. Following our teacher's lead, we joined in, at first soft and quavering; then, fortified by the heavily-accented baritones of the fathers in the audience, we all stood to lustily sing praise to our native land.

The last chord was our cue.

"M is for Mary," whispered Helen Walko, holding her "M" upside-down. Then, through to "S is for our Saviour," we blurted, whispered, rushed, and mumbled our "MERRY CHRISTMAS" recitations. We had opened the show!

It was our turn to sit on the papers on the floor to watch the rest of the programme and wait for the moment of our big surprise. It was the grade ones' special act, kept secret from even our parents, an act we had practised over and over for the past six weeks.

We had learned a dance—a Ukrainian dance. It was a splendid dance, done with four couples, all grade one students. The music was lively, with an exciting beat that made us hop higher and faster than we'd ever thought possible. But it was the costume that I loved best! Our skirts were made from bright pink crêpe paper, cut in even strips that allowed our bare legs to flash out wildly through the streamers as our partners swung us around and around. We were a vision as we whirled, our crêpe paper flying, vying with the brilliance of the lighted candles that we held aloft in sweaty hands throughout the dance. We heard the audience gasp, from both admiration and fear of fire, and soon heard applause—clapping and stamping that kept beat with our wild dance. We danced on! I could see, through a blur, that the audience was standing now and swaying along with us in rhythm with the power and beat of our un-Christmas-like dance. We stayed for wave after wave of encores, bowing and curtseying, our breath coming in hot, burning rasps,

Santa's horse all dressed up as a reindeer for a Saskatchewan school's Christmas concert.

perspiration gleaming on our bodies, high-lighted by our flickering, dripping candles.

Suddenly, the back door flew open and a cold blast of air burst into the room. And bells! We could hear bells! Yes, and laughter! Santa! It was Santa! A red suit blocked the doorway, fronted by a ponderous belly trimmed round with white fur. He threw back his head in a big roar of laughter, exposing two rows of perfect teeth.

"*Vesele Sviato, divchata i Khloptsi!*" he cried. His eyes were a snapping brown and his beard, shining black. "*Vesele Sviato!*" he bellowed again.

The children, numbed momentarily, now surged forward, grabbing at his sleeves, his belt, his big hand held out to us. "*Sviatyi Nykolai!*" they shouted, English forgotten.

"Santa! It's Santa Claus!" I heard myself say softly, and I ran forward to hold on to his sleeve, to accompany him as he lunged up to the front, his bumpy canvas bag rolling around on his massive shoulders.

He sat down—*oomph!*—on a chair placed near the Christmas tree and bent to untie the rope holding the big bag. His hand stopped and he looked up at us ringed round his chair. With a hearty laugh, he looked closely at the little package in his hand. "Shirlee!" he cried.

I edged onto his knee and looked into the smiling face edged with the bristling black beard.

"Vell!" he said, looking at me, suddenly serious. "And haf you been good gurl? Eh?" His mouth was wide, red, laughing. I grinned back, and suddenly it struck me: Santa was our neighbour, Pete Kuzenko, the one whose sleigh we had met at our gate. Santa was not some stranger who flew through the skies behind reindeer! We had followed him here to school. We had followed Santa!

"Oh, Santa . . . *Sviatyi Nykolai* . . .," I said, hugging him, feeling his whiskers scratch my forehead.

"You haf a goot time now, little gurl," he said as he gently pushed me from his knee. His black eyes, shining with kindness, are with me yet, when I remember.

We opened our presents near a pile of desks at the back of the room while the adults dismantled the stage and set benches along the walls, preparing for the dance. The band consisted of the teacher on the piano and three neighbourhood men, two playing fiddles and one, an accordian. After a quick tune-up, they broke with a loud "Hey!" into a fast-moving beat of a Ukrainian dance. This time, it was the adults' turn to take centre stage.

They danced, at first precisely with intricate steps, to music brought over from Galacia. I watched the women as they danced, women I knew as hard-working farm wives, now transformed into young-looking, brown-eyed maidens. They were laughing now, not caring that their hair fell from their neatly wrapped braids or "victory rolls" to trail in tendrils down their wet, shining necks. Their large, dark men whirled them, swirled them around the shiny oiled floor that had been sprinkled with sawdust to make it less slippery. Dust rose as the floor bounced and sprang in rhythm to their pounding feet, the dance becoming faster and wilder as song followed song. We kids slowly got up and danced with each other, stiffly bumping knees in vain imitation of the adults, avoiding each other's eyes while in such painful contact.

I noticed my parents standing quietly at the back of the school. My mother's eyes were shining, her head bobbing to the beat. My father stood beside her, looked quietly embarrassed by the antics of the people who kept bumping into him. My brother also stood silently watching, envious of the frivolity but too shy to join in. I nodded stiffly to them as my partner, Nick Olynick, jerked me past, then looked back towards the floor, losing my self-consciousness in the beat of the music and matching sway of my fellow dancers.

Mother's voice broke through my dream world. "Come on, dear, get your coat. Dad is getting the horse ready."

I was back suddenly in the hot, dusty one-room school, stuffing my sweaty arms into the cold sleeves of my coat, poking stiff legs into leggings and boots—boots that turned my dancer's feet into clumpy, black clods. I answered numbly to words of farewell shouted in both English and Ukrainian as we edged back through the knot of men standing on the outside steps cooling off with the help of a brown crock that passed back and forth among them.

The horse stood by the gate, stamping and chewing on her cold bit, impatient to get her job over with. She turned her head toward us and watched our approach through the restrictions of black leather eye-blinkers and the icing of frost that coated her eyelashes. My mother put the heated footwarmer underneath the fur robe and helped me climb up into the cutter and settle down into my seat. With a lurch, the sleigh swung out the gate and onto the long white road. I slipped down, down until the cold fur was tickling my cheeks, my breath flowing under the robe to make warm moisture. I turned my head slightly and looked out past the silent posts of the barbed-wire fences to the unblemished diamond-blanketed fields that rolled in a white wave to the ends of the earth. I laid my head back and looked up at the tiny stars, the moon now a small silver button. I stretched out my legs, still warm and tingling from dancing, and found the angled footwarmer near the bottom of the cutter. I closed my eyes. I could hear, far off now in the distance, the strains of the fiddles playing the dancing songs and the occasional shout of a dancer caught up in the joy of celebration. The rhythm of the mare's trotting feet matched the regular breathing of my family around me. I lay back quietly, allowing the sounds to hold me, and as I lay, rocked by the swaying motion of the cutter, the even beat of music and hooves and breathing floated out through the still, cold air. I realized that both my mother and I were humming. With lips closed against the cold, piercing air, each of us, lost in our private reveries, were humming the same melody—the never-to-be-forgotten strains of my wild Ukrainian dance.

I remember now, for these are the songs and memories of my childhood. They provide me yet with rhythm. They provide me with a soul!

10 | What a Character!

It didn't take the children very long to discover that every horse had a character and personality all of its own. Some ponies were kind; others, mean. Some were changeable; others developed persistent habits. A number learned very easily; others could be trained only with difficulty. Some were willing to share their oat bundles; other were so selfish they refused to permit another animal to come near them during feeding time. Some liked children and co-operated with them; others bided their time to bite, butt, or kick them. The broad range of human traits, both good and bad, was reflected in the horse population. They, likewise, had their good and bad days! Hence, to be a successful horseman or woman, the rural child learned the importance of making a study of each horse before attempting to handle it. Sometimes though, as among people, there developed a clash of personalities, and this incompatibility was detrimental to both youngster and beast.

Some horses were known as one-child animals, and although completely reliable as far as one particular juvenile was concerned, they became unmanageable in the hands of anyone else. It was strange to see a six-year-old girl ride a horse with ease, and the next moment, witness the same horse drop its head, flatten its ears, and buck until it had unseated a veteran rider. Certain ponies were so attached to their youthful masters that it was unwise to make a threatening gesture in the child's direction for fear of some reprisal by the horse. The majority of school horses, however, were so used to children that the youngsters could crawl between their hind legs and not be kicked or harmed in any way. It was not uncommon to see small children playing tag about the feet of an old school pony.

We Won Him in a Raffle

The acquisition of another school pony invariably precipitated a good deal of excitement and curiosity among the children of the family. They quickly sized up the relative strengths and weaknesses of the animal, then immediately began to beg their parents to permit them to try out the stranger. Only time and experience told whether the purchase had been a wise one.

A chap had been making the rounds of the Ensleaf S.D. (Buffalo, Alberta) one winter selling raffle tickets at fifty cents apiece on a small Indian buckskin. The man said he was dying and wanted money to visit a doctor. One of the girls of the Stone family had been sick most of that winter, so when the stranger called at their homestead, the mother, out of pure sympathy, bought a ticket for her ailing daughter. In due course, the youngster received the exciting news—she had won the prize! Then and there, the little girl decided to use the acquisition as her very own school pony.

When the Stones arrived in town to claim the animal, they discovered that, although it had only cost fifty cents, there was a livery stable bill against it as well as a one dollar fee for the halter. The horse itself was no bargain at any price! She was a buckskin Indian pony of around 630 pounds, slender, long-legged, well-aged (estimated in the upper twenties), and in possession of more vices than all the other horses put together that the Stones had ever owned.

The animal had a crooked neck, apparently caused by the shots that had been fired to capture her when she was part of a band of wild horses that had roamed the foothills country in the early days. Shooting was believed by some people to have been the strategy employed by Indians to catch the ponies, although there is more myth than truth to the theory. Horses were shot with a high-powered rifle through the grizzle just below the mane. The force of the impact stunned the animal long enough for the hunters to hog-tie their quarry. Once the animal revived, man's wit was pitted against the will of the horse to remain free. It required real courage and skill to break one of these wild ponies.

This particular buckskin had at least two other large scars on her neck, so it was assumed that she must have been of an extremely ferocious disposition during her youth. Although she went by the high-sounding Indian name of Napoos, the Stone children modified it to the more friendly Nappy.

Nappy was a halter puller and ruined more gear than the proverbial army. She was difficult to saddle, for she attempted to squeeze her handler in the stall, bit, swelled up, and became fidgety during the entire operation. Once saddled, Nappy did her best to prevent anyone from mounting her. If someone succeeded in getting on, she took off like the wind, relaxing her body so that the saddle girth instantly lost its tautness, and it was just a matter of time before the rider was dumped. Once she succeeded in getting rid of her

Ginny, a beautiful school horse, took Bill, Dave, and Helen Schellenberg to Aberdeen   *S.D. (Aberdeen, Saskatchewan) in 1940.*

jockey, she made a desperate attempt to escape. If she did, it was an entire day's job to catch her again. In fact, she was difficult to corner under the best of circumstances.

It didn't take the Stones very long to discover that it required two people to hitch Nappy to a buggy. Not only that, but the operation had to be performed against something solid, like a wall or corner fence; otherwise, the persnickety equine would back up indefinitely. Once someone got aboard, she shot forward like an arrow. About all the driver could do was to hold on.

Only one routine worked when they came to a gate. As they came near, one youngster slid off the buggy and unfastened the wire barrier, while the other child drove Nappy around in circles until the entrance was clear. Once the buckskin and buggy had passed through, the circuitous driving continued until the gate was made fast again. It was never wise to bring Nappy to a full stop, for she immediately went into reverse, jackknifed the vehicle, and soon upset it.

Occasionally, Nappy suffered a catch in her hind leg. Although the limb became as much as a foot longer than the other, it never seemed to have any adverse effect on her speed or cunning. She hippity-hopped for a mile or so and then levelled off again. She scorned affection and, for the most part, needed good, firm handling.

When Nappy got too old to drive the children to school, she was still useful on the farm. She brought the milk cows home all by herself, a distance of one and a half miles, just as efficiently as if someone were riding her.

For all her age, the stamina and craftiness of this little Indian pony were wonders to behold. Back and forth to school she had gone through the years, never a day absent when she was needed. The Ensleaf district will long remember the story of Nappy, the Indian pony.

Banned from the School Yard

In this mechanical age of school buses and automobiles, it is difficult to picture those times when horses were the only means of school transportation. Hence incidents involving horses, a favourite topic of conversation among farming folk, seem inconceivable today.

The Holdens of the Alexandra S.D. (Priddis, Alberta) were fortunate to own an old school pony who was really a treasure. Their small children often rode together, one behind the other, on this horse. If one fell off (and this was often), old Bob stood in the ditch and leaned right over to one side to help the tot climb on again. The family never really knew his age but estimated that he must have been thirty years old when he died.

The fun began when the Holdens purchased one of four donkeys that had been offered for sale by a circus when that particular act failed to attract the public.

In a field next to the schoolyard were half a dozen large, purebred Clydesdales that often leaned over the fence to enjoy the company of the school horses. It was customary to unsaddle or unharness the horses when they arrived at school and turn them loose in the yard until 3:30. The horses were, as usual, at the fence when, on her first day at school, Jenny came around the corner to introduce herself. She did! Her huge, furry ears alone were enough to scare them, but when she greeted them at the top of her voice, you'd have thought the Clydesdales had been entered in the Irish Sweepstakes judging from the spectacular and speedy manner in which they left that part of the country.

There was no need to have an Arbour Day cleanup at this school, for Jenny took care of that job by herself. She polished off all leftover lunches, pieces of orange peel, and scraps of paper lying about the schoolyard. Anyone eating in her presence had to bite off a piece of whatever it was and give it to her, or else she managed, by force, to take the whole thing.

Jenny's school days were cut short because the teacher did not care for the donkey's behaviour on three particular counts. First, if the Holden children were not out of the school promptly at 3:30, Jenny walked up to the schoolhouse door and loudly informed the teacher that her watch was slow. The braying continued until school was dismissed. Her second crime was following the teacher, who was scared of animals of any type, to the outhouse and staying near the doorway until something else attracted her attention. It was amazing how shortsighted the children were, for they never saw Jenny at moments like this. The third and most heinous offence was committed when Jenny tore the cover off the spare tire on the teacher's car—and ate it! From then on, the school board decreed that Jenny stay home.

Opposites Attract

When Orvina Black was eight years old, her brother Jarl, fourteen, traded a milk cow (worth about fifty dollars at that time) for a team of Welsh ponies. To describe them as a team was, however, an exaggeration—Pat and Mike were complete opposites.

Pat was a slightly lighter grey than Mike but a bit heavier in size. It didn't take me long to discover he was stubborn. Shortly after I learned to ride, I was dispatched to the pasture to bring in the milk cows. About half a mile along the way, Pat decided he wanted to go

Bill Woods and his faithful friend Ginger went to Vernon S.D. 3207 (Sibbald, Alberta) in 1941.

no further, so he walked up to the pasture fence and stood facing it. No amount of kicking, shouting, or slapping with the reins could move him. Jarl, who was watching from home, came out on Mike to give me a hand. When he mounted Pat, there was real action! Pat always seemed to sense when he had an inexperienced rider on his back. I remember my youngest sister, about fifteen years or so later, having the same problem. It was past time for her to arrive home from school, and we could hear her cries from the other side of the shelterbelt. On closer investigation, we found Pat leisurely feasting on some lush bromegrass while Audrey sat, flailing her

arms and legs to fight off swarms of voracious mosquitoes.

Mike, on the other hand, didn't seem to have a stubborn bone in his body. He never believed in wasting any time getting from one point to another. Once he started running, the rider had no choice but to hang on and hope to stay with him until he stopped. I remember a neighbour boy coaxing me on the way home from school one day to let him ride Mike. I could ride with his sister and brother in their cart. I reluctantly traded places with him. Our common road ended in a T, where we turned left and our neighbour turned right. We were in the habit of permitting our ponies to have their head on this homestretch, giving my brother, sister, and I a very fast ride and ending in an abrupt stop at the barn door. I warned Clarence he might not be able to stop Mike at the corner. He, however, was older and bigger than I was, so he was sure he'd have no problem. I must admit, it gave me a lot of self-satisfaction to watch Mike take the corner at full speed and Clarence hit the dust! He saved face by saying he jumped off.

Until I was about twelve years old, my younger brother, sister, and I shared the ponies, always riding one double. Eventually, I started to ride my older brother's saddle horse to school, so we each had a horse. Pat and Mike never held back and permitted the larger horse to take the lead.

We also had a two-wheeled cart that we used for school transportation in the summertime. It was roomy enough for the three of us and our school equipment. We drove Pat, who gave us a steady and safe ride. My father and

Jarl were the only ones who hitched Mike to the cart. They sat with a firm, strong hold on the reins and received a nonstop ride at a very fast trot!

Sometimes in the winter, he would hitch the team to a cutter to drive into town. Poor old Pat really had to put out to provide staying power to Mike's speed. We often made up verses for these special rides. One contained the following couplet:

Pat is slow and Mike is fast,
That is why their friendship lasts.

In the summertime, we kept the ponies in a small enclosure north of our trees. One morning we went out to catch them but couldn't find hide nor hair of them around the farm. We finally walked the two miles to school, and lo and behold, there were Pat and Mike in the schoolyard. They had crawled under our fence and strayed to school.

In fall and spring, the horses were turned loose in the schoolyard. Occasionally, Pat and Mike would amuse themselves by annoying the other horses and forcing them to scamper. They were small and quick, so they could get their nips and kicks in and then escape from the larger horses. Their teamwork was excellent!

In winter, the horses were kept in the school barn. We carried a bag of oats to feed them during their midday meal. Right after school, they were extremely anxious to head for home and didn't stand very patiently for us to mount. We rode bareback and could warm our hands by sitting on them. More often than not, we didn't have a bridle or a bit in their mouths. We merely used the halter and the rope they were tied with to control them.

Many, many times in the spring, we would arrive home soaked from the waist down. On our way home were a couple of sloughs along the road, which the ponies expressed a strong desire to visit for a drink. Since there was no water for them in the schoolyard, we were soft-hearted and yielded. Once they got their heads down and started drinking, they would gradually proceed out further from the edge and suddenly lie down! We knew this trick yet always had some silly notion that by pulling their heads up, we could prevent it.

Ours was the only team of ponies in our neighbourhood. They were invaluable! Besides riding to school, we rode to Northgate for music lessons, Sunday school, groceries, and the mail. They were swift and sure-footed for rounding up cows and horses. If we needed to take a shortcut and could lift the fence from the ground, the horses would crawl under. Then we would remount and go on our way!

Best of all, they were our loving and lovable friends. We spent hours brushing them, braiding manes and tails, and decorating their halters or bridles with wild flowers. The pair patiently submitted to my younger brother's "rodeos," which consisted of Roman riding, bucking broncs, lassooing, and herding cattle, besides providing rides for numerous kids through the years. We jealously guarded them from abuse. They loved treats such as sugar lumps, apples, and sweets. We rarely received a nickel in the dirty thirties to spend on an ice cream cone, but when we did, we'd eat the ice cream and the ponies got the cone. Their former owner lived in Northgate, and if she saw us, she'd insist we ride to her house so she could feed the ponies some bread and jam.

Long after we three were through with riding to school, our much-younger sister rode them. Pat and Mike lived to the ripe old ages of thirty-three and thirty-four years and remain a legend in our family.

It must have been a comfort to Jeanne's parents to see their small daughter on an equally small Shetland pony rather than a large Clydesdale workhorse. The two, a perfect match, went to school together every day in Birdtail Valley, Manitoba, in 1945.

From Lazy and Slow to Big and Ugly

Margaret (Crisford) Norris and her brother, Arthur, drove a whole string of different school ponies to Highland Park S.D. 2519 (Sibbald, Alberta). Each one was a unique individual, though in some cases, this was not a compliment.

Strange to say, Nobby had been with us all my life but, for reasons that escaped my young mind, was not favoured as a workhorse. He was considered lazy and slow and didn't pull his share. Even so, this black

gelding became our next school horse. We were nervous, and he was cross, but necessity settled us into a good relationship, and eventually we were able to pound him into some semblance of speed. Occasionally he would decide not to face a sandstorm or a snowstorm, but by then we were experienced enough to change his mind. Nobby committed suicide by bloating on an excess of grain—quite a feat in those years of poor crops.

How to get to school now? A neighbour lent Dad a good-sized Shetland pony. The thought of driving such a small horse at our age was an outrage! Even so, home he came and worked his way right into our hearts. He came equipped with harness, cart—and a warning that we would have to teach him who was boss. Sure enough, the first few days we travelled at a slow crawl. We thought this was because he was so small and the miles so long, which was exactly what he wanted us to think. Dad told us he could do better. We eventually discovered that Shetlands really have great endurance and can trot right along. The little fellow was only with us for half a year, but I had fun riding him bareback after school and regretted seeing him go home in June.

He was replaced with our final horse, Flossy. She was a big, rather ugly mare who possessed no redeeming qualities save her trustworthiness and an ability to trot right along. She soon knew the road better than we did. Most of the time the reins could be left dangling while we engaged in fighting, reading, or whatever. One morning, however, my brother touched her with the whip and caught her in the withers. Bang! She lashed out with both feet, hitting the buggy like a rocket. The tugs broke and away went Flossy, but without the buggy. Luckily, she didn't go far, as our frantic "whoas!" had their effect. I think we fashioned something out of binder twine and my dress belt that still made it possible to reach school before nine o'clock.

Highland Park School closed that year. Arthur left home to work, so for one year, I rode Flossy across the pastures and deserted farmlands to a neighbouring school, Vernon S.D. 3207 (Sibbald, Alberta). Halfway there,

I'd meet up with another classmate, Bill Woods, and we'd ride along together. His horse, Ginger, was a much classier mount, and younger, but old Flossy had her pride too. We kept up, be it a gallop, trot, or walk. When galloping across the prairie with the wind in your face, you tend to forget what your horse looks like and can imagine anything you wish. Times being what they were in those adverse years, I wasn't likely to own a better horse.

God Made No Two Alike

Shetland ponies may be small, but what they lack in size they make up for in determination, speed, and endurance. They are, nevertheless, tempermental creatures. Ruby (Plomp) Anderson rode over six different Shetland ponies to school in La Riviere, Manitoba between 1936 and 1943, when she graduated from high school.

I lived two miles from a four-room setup in the village of La Riviere, Manitoba, in the scenic Pembina Valley. While all others used buggy or cutter transportation, I was the only pupil to ride horseback to school.

Ruby Plomp leaving for Podolia S.D (La Riviere, Manitoba) in 1943 on one of her six Shetland ponies.

I carried a small bag of oats, along with my five-pound Bee Hive syrup lunch pail, for our noon-hour snacks. Sometimes when going to town, we would drop off some hay or straw for bedding at the school barn.

King, my first pony, was brought out of retirement from the valley pasture for me to ride as he was old, faithful, and used to youngsters. I learned, in one lesson, how to ride a horse. Bravely, we started off that first morning, with one mile to travel along a main highway and another mile on a seldom-used valley trail. All of a sudden, King took it into his head to revisit his retirement pasture and, forgetting his age, took me at a swift gallop across the field. Seeing my plight (and hearing my screams), one of the men tore after us on horseback and redirected King toward the school.

When King retired to his reward, I rode a sturdy mare by the name of Dolly. Every so often, we enjoyed an uneventful trip to school, but those rare occasions do not stand out in my mind. This impatient horse, anxious to get home after a long day in the school barn, would seldom wait for me to mount by conventional means (using an upturned pail, fencepost, or woodpile). Instead, with bridle and halter dangling, she would dash off home, leaving me to walk. There, at the barnyard gate, she would be waiting patiently for me to let her in to enjoy the water trough and haystack!

At other times, when I fell off into a snowbank (which occurred frequently while plunging up and down in snowdrifts after a storm, when she was first to break the road), she would wait for me to climb back on. Did she, perhaps, remember that on such occasions she was rewarded, on arriving home, with a handful of oats?

Queenie's most notable characteristic was to stop dead in her tracks at the least provocation, sending me flying over her head. One morning as we galloped to school in high gear, a flock of birds flew from a roadside bush and frightened Queenie to a dead halt. I was thrown forward, landing with a thump on my back. To add insult to injury, before I could get up, the mare had returned home, leaving me to limp homeward at the end of the day.

Silver, the streaker, brings back memories of a different sort. She absolutely hated anything with wheels on it. Initially, she shied away from vehicles, but she eventually decided to chase them. Those were some of my fastest rides! How I prayed we would make the highway-mile without encountering any sort of vehicle. Whenever I saw or heard one, I'd try turning her head so she couldn't see it, but the minute she heard it, the chase was on! Sometimes, to avoid one of these escapades, I would quickly jump off and tie her to the nearest telephone pole or fencepost.

After much complaining about these wild rides, I was informed I could ride spirited Star instead. From my daily observations, I concluded that his one and only speed was *slow!* There was no way I could get him to hurry. None of my usual tricks to get us to school on time succeeded. It appeared he would not be dominated by a mere female rider, for I often noticed that when one of the men rode him to fetch the cows or to check the fields or fox ranch, they disappeared like the wind! Nevertheless, he took me safely to and from school, ofttimes through rain, wind, heat, storms, and cold. Even when I could not see the way in a blinding blizzard, my "guiding Star" got us safely home.

Dolly's colt, Dimple, was now broken in and ready for school. Her favourite trick was stepping on my feet then gently sliding off. She was slim, sleek, and speedy—she barely gave me time to get on and away she'd go!

Even after seven years of being transported to and from the La Riviere School, I never felt as though I could trust any one of those ponies. They were endearing but oh, how tricky! Like human beings, each had his or her own characteristics. God made no two alike!

Our Indian Ponies

Of the twenty-three horses Bessie Dulmage's family owned over the years, there were two the family prized above all others. Both were Indian ponies, and they were very special; neither, however, was without his peculiarities.

One of our Indian ponies, Dick, was indeed a very clever animal! Dad insisted, when travelling up hills (one, in particular, that was long and winding), that we all—with the exception of my small sister and the driver—

climb out of the buggy and walk. There was an infinite number of imaginary slopes at which he grunted, groaned, and stopped until we unloaded his cargo.

I recall how cunning and difficult to catch he was. We learned to leave his halter on, hoping to gain some advantage. We'd rattle a basin of oats, and he'd appear for a mouthful. Then, quick as a flash, he'd run away—unless you managed to grab his halter! He served as our cow pony, rounding up the milkers, and he knew how to separate the young stock from them. Ofttimes, however, he would grow impatient and nip their behinds!

Dick died in 1928 at the age of thirty-seven years. He became paralysed and a neighbour mercifully shot him out by the straw stack. Needless to say, we weren't in the mood to attend the box social in the schoolhouse that night; we were in mourning!

Charlie, our other Indian pony, was a buckskin colour. He was homely, mean, and ate lots but always looked scrawny. He had a nasty habit of biting and chasing us. Perhaps he couldn't be blamed for nipping us; after all, two passengers was sufficient, and when a third got a leg up, he'd rebel! He died of natural causes soon after Dick's departure.

The proportions were right: Jean Speers on Guss and her smaller brother Larry on Molly, *on their way to Highland Park S.D. 2519 (Sibbald, Alberta) in the thirties.*

Walter's Cussedness

In the 1940s, the Bauman family of Landdonville, Alberta, came to know and, yes, love a master of trickiness named Walter. Walter was a particular trial to Joyce (Bauman) Reid and her twin brother, Jack.

When I was a little girl, we never had a horse that was strictly for riding; our big, faithful workhorses had to perform double duty. Yet I always dreamed we would obtain a riding horse—and he would be wonderful! I imagined him to be a sleek, black, long-legged, majestic-looking horse that I would name something elegant like Major, Prince, or Lightning. Unfortunately, when we finally did obtain a riding horse, he was a stubby, short-legged, ornery bay gelding and went by the common name of Walter!

Dad bought him because my sister, Doris, had taken as many grades as she could at our Telegraph S.D. and would now have to attend Louise Lake S.D., some four miles away from our farm. There were no school buses then,

so she would have to ride horseback. Dad instructed her on the care of Walter and admonished her not to ride him too hard and get him heated. Unfortunately, Doris loved to sleep in and always left for school at the last possible moment. The neighbours reported seeing her walking or trotting sedately along until out of sight of our farm and then riding like the wind the rest of the way to school.

The next year, Doris went to school in Dewberry, so Walter came into the joint custody of my twin brother, Jack, and me. We were quite small. Dad said he would prefer we rode bareback as he was afraid we wouldn't be able to cinch the saddle tightly enough and, once we were galloping along, the saddle would slip and we would be hurt. He was right, too—not because we were too small, but because Walter was so cussed! When we approached him with the saddle, he'd inhale and puff out his belly and not exhale until after we'd cinched up and climbed on. After several episodes with the saddle upside-down under his belly, we soon learned the cure. Just as we were ready to tighten the cinch, we'd poke him sharply. He'd exhale, and we'd finish the job.

We usually rode bareback to school in fall and winter as it was much warmer that way. My brother could clamber on without requiring anything to stand on, but I always needed a booster. Usually, there was nothing around other than the barbed-wire fence. Jack would steer Walter parallel to the fence, and I'd balance on the second row of the railing, clasp his mane, and swing onto his back. Walter's timing was perfect! Just as I swung my leg over his back, he'd turn his head and nip my exposed backside. After having been nipped a time or two, I became very gun-shy, so when I was ready to mount, I did a lot of shouting: "Walter, you so-and-so, don't you dare!" or, "Walter, you bite me and you'll be on your way to the glue factory!"

In winter we took a short cut through pastures and fields. Granted, we had less distance to travel, but annoyingly, we had to open as many as nine gates. We took turns sliding off to open the gates and clambering back on. The moment the person remaining on Walter's back rode through the opening, he'd once again display his perfect timing and cussedness. The moment you were opposite the gatepost, he'd swerve and rub your leg against the post. This trick never led to a serious leg injury, but many a lard-pail lunch bucket was smashed beyond repair thanks to the vengeful streak in his personality!

When the weather got very cold, we would be so bundled up we couldn't see. No problem! Walter knew the way. He plodded along, and when he stopped, we knew we were at another gate. Once, we rode him through a huge snowbank and he got stuck. His short legs couldn't reach the top crust of the snow, so he floundered and became frightened. We had a terrible time getting him out, using just our hands to clear the snow away.

Walter was quite subdued during the winter season. He moved slowly and begrudgingly along the route in the morning, but in the evening, he moved along briskly in anticipation of reaching the warm barn. In spring, however, all his pent-up exuberance came out in full glory. He was a brute to catch! We would proceed to the pasture with his bridle, and in our most ingratiating voice, we'd call him. He would always come prancing up to us! We'd reach for his mane, and he'd snort, wheel, and race off in big circles, tantalizingly close to us, but never quite close enough to be caught. If we went back to the barn to renew our supply of grain, if he tired of running, and more importantly, if he felt like it, he would come to thrust his nose in the bucket. If we worked quickly, we would finally catch him.

Riding to school during the other seasons, we had to go the long way around on the road. Here we would join other schoolmates on their horses. Inevitably, this would inspire horse races. If other horses were ahead of us, no amount of coaxing could entice Walter to catch up or overtake them. On the other hand, if he was ahead and heard horses running behind him, he would take off like a jack rabbit! He'd take the bit in his teeth, which rendered all our pulling on the reins quite useless, and we'd be left hanging there as we flew down the road. Riding bareback, this usually meant that by the time he finally tired or we finally stopped him, Jack and I had bounced right up onto his neck—right behind his ears! On other days, he would behave himself until we were in sight of the barn. Then he'd take off like a shot and gallop right through the barn doorway. It was either duck or be wiped off! And ducking isn't easy when you're riding double!

In spite of his cussedness, we loved Walter dearly. We rode him double to school, but individually, we rode him to get the mail at the mailbox a mile and a half away, bring in the cows, visit friends on other farms, or just for fun. Walter really was quite an adept cutting horse as he neck-reined very well and was just as ornery as the cows! On top of all this, he was quite clever. Jack taught him to nod his head up and down on a signal for a "yes" answer and to shake it back and forth for a "no" reply. We also taught Walter to count by pawing the ground with his hoof.

I spent so much time riding horseback that it disgusted my oldest sister. Before her dates would arrive, she would make Mother promise to keep me from coming in from horseback riding until after her date had gone. She maintained that I "smelled horsey." I could never understand why that upset her as I couldn't see what was so unpleasant about a horsey smell.

Through the years, people have expressed surprise that I never learned how to ride a bicycle. I always reply that I didn't need a cold, inanimate bicycle. Instead, I had a very individualistic horse, who was my friend, my confidant, my transportation, and who kept me warm in winter, besides.

Shortly after Jack and I went away to high school in Vermilion, Mother and Dad sold the farm and moved north. As there were no children left at home to ride him, Walter was sold. A great deal of love went with him. I hope that, for many years, he continued to astonish, aggravate, and endear himself to his new owners, as he did to us.

From Stunt Pony to School Pony

Spot was an unusual horse, a pinto pony that, besides being an able cow horse, had done tricks for his master's stunt riding. Spot had a love for children and was "retired" to being a kid's school horse. Gustav Eriksson was glad to find such a good horse for his small youngsters, and Spot came to his farm in about 1927.

Spot would dawdle along sleepily, then suddenly shy sideways and tumble us to the ground. He would even make us walk home, while he kept ahead of us, stealing a nibble of grass and continuing to dodge us. We also learned that, sometimes, if we cried loudly or played lame, he pitied us and let himself be caught and mounted again. With an adult, he could be extremely hard to bring in from the pasture, leading the entire herd of horses away from the corners and corrals where they would likely be caught. Occasionally when we brought home the cows to milk, he would become cross at some cow and pursue it at

Rita (Desilets) Galarneau, ready to start the seven-mile trip to Connorsville S.D. *(Sunnynook, Alberta) in 1935.*

great speed, turning sharply, stepping quickly, and biting the cow several times before it fled for home. No cow could dodge him!

Spot lived to be a great age for a horse; his mother was reputed to have reached forty years. After he retired from the Eriksson family, he went to the August Long children who, with other neighbourhood children, probably learned to ride on this trusty pony.

128

11 | A Tribute to Faithful Friends

Today the school pony is no more. The roar of the yellow school bus has replaced the rattle of the buggy and the rhythmic beat of the horses' hooves on the prairie trail. The wild flowers, birds' nests, baby ducks, gophers, bees, sloughs, frogs, snakes, and the wild strawberries are still there, but the rural children, cooped up in the yellow school bus, cannot stop to enjoy them. The bus has a schedule to maintain.

Only in the hearts of those who remember the days of the Little White Schoolhouse does the school horse still live. And there, his glory will never fade.

What A Deal!

Evelyn Blanche Hayback and her sister walked two long miles to Eureka S.D. (Ponoka, Alberta) and back every day. All that changed when they got Tommy. The two girls rode him to school for ten years, from 1924 to 1934. Tommy was responsible for Evelyn's lifelong love of horses, which, at seventy, is as strong as ever.

How excited we were! We now had a pony, but we didn't get a chance to ride him for awhile. He was a long-legged dark bay, once strong, sturdy, and tough. But when we first saw him, he could hardly carry his own weight around, let alone a rider. All he desired was a little food and an opportunity to eat it, although at times, he was almost beyond caring for such essentials. This pony had travelled all the way from Montana that fall when his owner found work on a farm in Alberta. The old pony was turned out to rustle with about twenty workhorses. He wasn't able to hold his own against the sleek, black Percherons, so when we first saw him, he was a sorry sight indeed. Imagine a pony, very, very thin, black, and scrawny, sporting raw sores where vicious teeth had doffed some of the skin. He was tired, stiff, and disabled, his head hung low, and his eyes were dull and lifeless.

His owner, realizing what was happening to his faithful servant and knowing that my sister and I walked two miles to school every day, came to visit my father and offered to sell Tommy to him for ten dollars. He assured us the animal was a good school pony. Although my father at first refused, he relented when Mr. Newell wanted to give him to us for the sake of a good home. My dad handed over the ten dollars, and we had a pony!

Seldom has anyone received such value for their money! As life and strength returned to that poor skeleton, we found that we had a really remarkable horse. How I wish we could roll back the curtain to see what kind of training he had undergone. There wasn't a thing he didn't know about herding cattle. He could start very quickly, which gave him an advantage in school races until he stiffened with age. There wasn't a school horse in the country that could beat him. He clamped the bit firmly in his teeth, and about all the rider could do was to hang on. What a thrill to mount such a fast horse in a race! It's a wonder we didn't all break our necks.

Tommy could also stop short, as every good cow pony must, and many were the jolts and tumbles we took as we were learning to ride. The pony would shy most unexpectedly and then carefully assist us in picking ourselves up and climbing back into place again. He lowered his head and, once the rider draped himself around his neck, would toss him up, thus sliding the equestrian back to the proper place. The rider needed only to swing one leg over and sit upright, ready to go again. Tommy used to stand up on his hind legs like a dog begging if the reins were pulled just right, or buck if the heels were dug in at the right place on his flanks. This horse could be ridden without bridle, saddle, halter, or even a rope and could be guided by pressure of the knees or by leaning forward and slapping the side of his neck.

Tommy became fat and lazy after a few months of good food and care, thus amply ful-filling his former owner's promise of being a good school pony. During the ten years we had Tommy, he rarely missed a school day. As there were too many of us to ride one horse, he pulled a buggy or a cutter most of the time. Only twice do I remember him failing to get us to school and home again, and then he didn't really balk: Once was when he waded into snowbanks which were so crusted that he was, more or less, hanging on his stomach; the other was in a dust storm so thick one couldn't see a hand held only a foot in front of the eyes. In the first instance, we had to unhitch Tommy and return home, leaving the cutter. A team of those strong Percherons had to be called in to break the trail. During the dust storm, he led willingly, although the buggy vibrated so badly from the wind that

Margaret Gubkine's father built this rig for her and her brother in 1933. The two had to travel four miles to school near Ranfurly, Alberta.

no one dared ride in it. We slowly stumbled along until we reached a neighbour's. We were a sorry sight indeed but otherwise arrived unscathed. At home, however, a hayrack was tipped off the wagon and clothes were blown into the bushes from the line.

Sometimes in winter, we used a big stock saddle, so while one child was riding, the rest of us could hang on to a rope and ski to school. This operation was fun, and we were quite peeved at one watcher, who told our mother we would make much faster time if we walked. Of course, no one wanted to ride the horse, so the job fell to the youngest on the way to school. We took turns on the way home. Maybe the strong arms and balance required had some bearing on the fact that three of the boys became sailors during World War II. I've often wondered what Tommy thought of this kind of ropework after the cattle roping he had been trained to do.

Tommy loved bread, cake, sugar, and tobacco! When he was allowed the freedom of the schoolyard with the other horses, he learned to come to the schoolhouse begging for crusts. Yes, he even put his head in the open window at noon, which caused some merriment among the pupils. However, the teacher put an end to this when Tommy started coming during school hours and, if the window was closed, rubbing his nose up and down on the glass pane. This was too much for her patience to endure.

In another instance, the tables were turned. Teacher was pleased and school boys cross about the fondness Tommy had for school lunches. These were supposed to be eaten at noon and not during recess, but some of the boys, ignoring the rule, hid their lunches outside. However, after losing them to a dog when hidden in the rock foundation and to Tommy when hung in a tree, the boys gave up. They left their lunches inside the school where the food belonged.

Tommy was very fond of water, especially on hot days when sweat and mosquitoes made him itchy. It was very common for him to stop in a pond or ditch and start pawing with one front foot, sending the water splashing on everything around. Then, if one happened to be riding bareback, Tommy would lie down in the water and roll over. There was no alternative but for the driver to scramble to safety and walk home, leading a dirty but smug pony.

When our family concluded its time at our country school, a neighbour borrowed old Tommy for his children, who were just starting at a different school. One day he came strolling home, obviously so overjoyed to be back that we never let anyone take him again. Thus he retired, only pressed into service for the sake of small visitors, whose antics he seemed to enjoy whether they hung on, thrilled and a bit scared at being on a real, live horse for the first time, or whether they scrambled on and off every which way, sometimes five or six at a time.

At times, he was the only horse in the pasture. He stayed close to the cows and brought them home whenever he wanted to come himself. He would come walking sedately behind them down the lane, his head bobbing and his big ears flapping with every step, carefully herding the stragglers. Tommy's teeth finally failed, and he died at the age of twenty-four years; he had opened the feed bin once too often and got too much grain.

We Crushed His Spirit

This story of a sorrel, named Frank, leads one to argue that horses do indeed have feelings!

In a rural district near Saskatoon, Saskatchewan, two sisters drove their pony to a country school two and a half miles away. Frank had been in the family for a good number of years and at one time had formed a part of an excellent driving team—the pride and joy of their father. The horse had a genuine instinct for gentleness where children were concerned. If they overtook fellow students as they drove to school, the girls did not need to pull the reins to stop Frank. He invariably paused long enough for the newcomers to climb aboard. It was intriguing to watch Frank turn his head to see how the loading was progressing. On one occasion,

The Hope children en route to Red Deer Lake S.D. (Red Deer, Alberta) in 1917. Big sister had to handle the reins and all the books and lunches; her little brothers just had to hang on!

Frank had stopped so often to pick up pupils walking to school that by the time he had reached his destination, he was pulling the entire school population of eleven students.

Anytime this horse heard another vehicle coming up from the rear, he pulled aside into the ditch, of his own accord, and remained stationary until the other outfit passed by. Frank was also a perfect gem when there were interesting things for the girls to do while they were travelling to school. He waited patiently, nibbling whatever grass he could find, while his youthful passengers picked strawberries, gathered crow's eggs, tossed rocks at the frogs in the slough, or perhaps captured some baby ducks, which they tucked away in their lunch buckets. Frank never so much as raised an eyebrow at these rather dubious pursuits. He minded his own business and never meddled.

Eventually, the time arrived when it was decided that Frank should be retired to pasture. The family purchased a horse of gentle reputation to replace him. This was way beyond his comprehension! For a solid week, he left on his own punctually at eight o'clock, went to his familiar stall in the school barn, and remained there all day, untied, until 3:30. Finally, he reluctantly resigned himself to his fate and discontinued the practice.

Late that same fall, when the harvest was over and the fences were down, the family received a phone call from a farmer whose land adjoined the school. Did they know that Frank was at the schoolhouse? The older boys were dispatched to bring him home. Next morning, the family found Frank dead in the barnyard. Had he known that his last days were upon him and made his final trip to the little old schoolhouse, the scene of so many of his happy memories, to bid farewell? The entire household was broken-hearted because they were positive that they had crushed Frank's spirit and were thus responsible for his demise.

Bingo Was a Two-Generation School Horse

Bingo was his name! He was a bay with black mane and tail, light enough to be a saddle horse, yet heavy enough to be a standby for any wagon, plough, binder, or stoneboat requiring an extra horse for an hour or a day. Bingo was born on the Cole homestead, twenty-five miles north of Coronation, Alberta, in 1916. Jesse Cole rode him, as a young horse, to Mount Lookout and Fairfield schools, each a distance of four miles away. In September of 1937, Bingo started school again, sporting a rebuilt saddle of home-tanned leather and a homemade bridle. Jesse's sons, Gerald, then Ronald and Allan in turn, attended Fairfield and Bonny Doone schools.

Bingo was not a fast horse, and he seldom won any races, but he *was* dependable—so dependable that, if he ever gained his freedom, due to an untied halter shank or an open gate, he always returned home and stood at his own barn door. This proved to be a real asset when a second person required a ride to school but was to be delivered later by other means. You could simply take his bridle off, tie it over the saddle, and send Bingo home. If a serious blizzard erupted during the school day, all we needed to do was pull a gunnysack over our heads. (We didn't know what parkas were, and a sack was usually part of the saddle blanket ensemble.) Bingo instinctively knew the way home, plodding along through the drifts, waiting at unopened gates, and finally stopping outside the barn door. This animal never lost his way—a comforting thought to the family waiting at home.

I remember one Hallowe'en night—in fact, it was two o'clock in the morning! Two friends and I had a fun-filled and eventful evening doing the schoolyard and all our nearby neighbours' yards up good, after having been cautiously forewarned at home never to cause destruction or injury. Upon returning to the poplar bluff where our horses were so carefully hidden away, we were astounded to discover only their halters—three of them, tied in a row. There could be no doubt about Bingo's whereabouts: he would be standing at the barn door at that very moment! The moon had just vanished from the sky. One tired boy faced a three-mile walk home, while the other two lads had four miles to cover, all in different directions.

Bingo was truly a multi-purpose horse. In addition to transportation duties, Bingo was well acquainted with the routine pickup and delivery of mail, which arrived twice weekly at the Puffer Post Office. Mrs. Lydia Lamont,

Babe took Bill and Dave Schellenberg to Aberdeen S.D. from 1928 to 1940.

the postmistress, always had the rolls of mail, carefully tied with binder twine from straw stacks, ready after school. These were carefully positioned in our homemade canvas bag with leather drawstrings and hung over the saddle horn. Bingo knew the route and the familiar short cuts we used to leave mail with a number of shut-in neighbours, often carrying messges from one neighbour to another.

In winter the various trails to school through the parkland afforded us hunting and trapping opportunities, and Bingo knew where to stop and wait at every set. Spring brought new stopovers along the way for our horse. Crow and magpie eggs were collected and sold. And why not put a setting crow to use? A magpie was able to set on two hen's eggs, three crow's, and four hawk's. On the hatching date, our little brother, Allan, not yet at school, would ride along with us on Bingo, then walk home with the newly hatched nestlings in a basket. Three cents for crow's eggs from the municipality and five cents for each chick was indeed big money. Bingo always provided the transportation, often standing below a nest while we balanced on his back peering into the nest or reaching for a higher branch.

The end of the school day meant a procession of children travelling together in any one direction on foot, horseback, bicycle, or skis according to the season. Why walk if a ride was available? Bingo was often required to carry seven or more children between mane and tail. If a person could get up and hang on, he got a ride, while those who owned skis were pulled behind on a rope. This system, however, required that the first person off sit farthest back on Bingo's rump, and usually he found himself off and walking again before he had actually intended to do so.

Only once did Bingo let his riders down. It was a very hot day in June. On the way home, we watered our horses at the first slough near the schoolyard by riding out into the water. One of the horses lay down and rolled over. The others, including Bingo, decided to follow! What chaos! There was yelling, shouting, crying, and screaming; books, paper, pencils, floating lunch containers, and drenched children were scattered everywhere. The horses quickly jumped to their feet, and those who had managed to keep reins in hand were able to catch the loose horses.

Sunday morning, it was back to the schoolhouse again for Bingo—this time as one of a team of horses on the stoneboat or sleigh to take the family to Sunday school and church.

At home it was the job of faithful Bingo to pull the garden cultivator up and down each row. He was the buggy horse in summer and the little red cutter horse in winter, whether carrying children to school or providing Mother with transportation to the ladies' missionary meeting. Bingo's pulling of the one-horse buggy had special implications for us children as well. By driving Bingo out into a slough, we could fill a barrel with water. Then we would drive out into the pasture to drown out the gophers. Our dog, Jack, loved the sport, and Bingo knew just where to stop at each gopher hole and would remain calm whenever a soggy gopher tried to take refuge under his ungulae.

The war effort brought a new responsibility for Bingo and his buggy—helping to collect twenty-three hundred pounds of used rubber with the Fairfield School children, for which they won the prize offered by the Castor School Division for the most rubber collected. It was also Bingo who provided transportation for collecting bones for the war effort, including the last horned skulls of the magnificent buffalo.

In 1945, our family moved to Clive, Alberta, where high school education was accessible. Bingo could never be left behind.

He adjusted well, never attempting a return to his former home. School trips were infrequent now as the family lived only a mile from school. He continued to be the ever-faithful garden and cow horse, with an occasional trip for the mail, until his death at thirty-two years. Young and old alike shed tears, with much thanksgiving for such a kind animal friend. Bingo, you were the best pet this family ever had!

A Living Memorial

As the days of the Little White Schoolhouse gradually fade into the past, so too will the days of the old school horse, but Jean Billett of the Wide Awake S.D. (Indian Head, Saskatchewan) feels their Minnie stands out as a living memorial of that faithful breed.

She became part of our lives thirteen years ago when we bought her from a neighbour who recommended her as a dependable school horse. She was a horse of twenty-seven years then; today, she is thirty-eight. Her sleek bay coat, thick black mane and tail, and the alert arch of her neck belie her age. She has a workhorse build but has never been used as such. It fell to her to tote howling, screaming children back and forth from the Little White Schoolhouse, which she did with very calm reserve.

The eight children of the Billett family took their turns driving Minnie to school through the years, but I have reason to believe that it was really Minnie who took them.

Her gait depended on the direction and the climate. Going off in the morning, she seemed as reluctant to get to school as the children were; at home time, however, the last foot was hardly off the ground before she was homeward bound. A hot, sultry day called for a more leisurely pace. On such a day, Minnie was sighted plodding across a field after school with a seemingly empty buggy. On closer inspection, it was discovered that the two young occupants had stretched out on the seat and floor of the buggy for a nap! On another occasion, while being directed in a different, roundabout route, all the shouting and jerking on the lines were of no use—she still insisted on the usual cross-country trail and jogged along in what appeared to be a stubborn mood. On hearing this, I felt a little disappointed in Minnie because she had defied orders. My faith was soon restored when I realized that the reins were not hooked to the bridle, and hitched in this way, she could feel no direction from the lines, proving that when youth fails, Minnie carries on.

In later years, Minnie was the only school horse to make the daily trip to our country school, and her many admirers awaited her coming. Eager and loving hands helped unhitch her and escort her to the stall in the old school barn. Finding herself dependent on thoughtless youth, she sometimes waited in vain for her noonday feed. The bale of choice hay would sit, forgotten, in the back of the buggy. The young driver would discover it at home time and, fearing it would show proof of negligence, would toss it into an empty stall. Quite a few bales would collect, a silent reminder of Minnie's forgotten dinners. But Minnie held no grudges and performed her task unstintingly. She did not, however, believe in pampering, and she pulled no punches. She thought it quite proper to wander off in the direction of home during

school hours if her young attendant forgot to tether her securely when she was allowed in the pasture on fine summer days. Patience was put to the test as a weary, dust-laden boy trudged after her. Despite what he thought of her exasperating behaviour, she had to be coaxed in the most appealing manner before she would allow a hand to be laid on her.

The youths, just newly grown-up, looked down on Minnie as a mode of conveyance and talk of speedways and sports cars. But as they reminisce about the days she carted them to and fro, it is quite evident that they have happy memories forever embedded in their hearts. She was their first real responsibility.

Jean Johnson riding Mabel and sister Beatrice being pulled along behind on a *toboggan with the school's water supply.*

Many a happy and carefree time was spent with Minnie, but there were also tears. In the few upsetting incidents that did occur, she was found blameless and always kept her head when all about her were losing theirs. A rein pulled too short when going out the gate would mean a tangle of barbed wire, buggy, and posts and many tears. Then the oldest one, no matter how young, took command of the situation, and Minnie would calmly nibble grass till tears were dried and all was sorted out and in order again. Tears never meant injury but rather, surprise and fright, which were a good springboard to a very spectacular story for the retelling. She gave our youngest three the surprise of their lives the day she dropped in her tracks within a short distance of the school. Down she went, headfirst, breaking the buggy shaft and twisting her neck in a very grotesque manner. The young occupants scrambled out in shocked horror. Our youngest, a first-grader, broke into tears. The second youngest, trembling from head to foot, tried to console him. The oldest, a sixth-grader, made a beeline for the school telephone. His tense, high-pitched voice shrieked out the terrible happenings—that Minnie was either dead, or at best, she had broken her neck. Meanwhile, back at the scene of the accident, Minnie unscrambled herself and with a few brisk shakes, quickly regained her composure. By the time we arrived to appraise the situation, all was serene. The frightened young had been gathered into the security of their classes. Down at the barn, Minnie was quietly chewing on some hay. The only evidence of the incident was the broken buggy shaft and Minnie's skinned nose. She tossed her head as we peered in at her as much as to say, "Oh, skip it!" I must confess that, through loyalty to Minnie, I was tempted not to record this incident. The cause of her stumble is a mystery, but it did not detract from the trust we had in her.

Back and forth she went through the years, never a day absent when she was needed. Like old-time teachers who work to nearly the last day, Minnie was not to be outdone. She kept her secret well! After all, who would have guessed, at the age of thirty-one years, that three days after her school duties were done, she would give birth to a filly colt in the pasture. The adults were surprised, and the children, delighted. In six weeks she was ready to step back into the harness and the usual school-day routine again, with her young colt, Penny, frolicking along at her

Dean Courts and her trusty school pony, Dora, in the forties.

139

side—incidentally, not far from the generous supply of nourishment. Minnie took this dual role in stride, keeping everybody happy by always putting first things first.

Daisy Was a Professional

Karen (Christensen) Kam remembers her father buying what was advertised as a "professional" school horse to take his children to Thistle Dale S.D. (Borden, Saskatchewan). Over the years, the Christensen children discovered that this was indeed the case.

She began transporting us to school when JoAnn, the oldest of four children, was in grade three and Carl, in grade two. Our mom was, at first, concerned about our safety, so she took Daisy and the two youngsters on a dry run. After the first day, Daisy knew her way to the one-room school four and a half miles away. Soon, the four of us were making the trip, either perched on the cart or snuggled in the cutter, both of which our dad had constructed for us.

What times we had! Regardless of the weather or season, there were few worries that Daisy would be unable to get us to school and home again.

One day our youngest brother, Ernie, decided to ride Daisy. He had never been on a horse before and being rather small, was unable to clamp his short little legs tightly around Daisy's ample middle. He fell off! In the confusion, the horse accidentally stepped on him. Ernie's terrified screams were mostly due to his wounded pride, but Daisy didn't know that—and that was the end of anyone riding her! She never permitted anyone on her back again.

Once, when we were half a mile from school, Daisy suddenly lowered her head, thrust her ears back, turned around, and headed for home at a gallop. There, behind us, was a billygoat with its head down. Daisy wasn't taking any chances! Needless to say, we were late. But what a story we had to tell!

Another day, Daisy stopped dead in her tracks and refused to budge. She always refused to move if her halter shank fell down or if some section of the harness broke. We jumped out of the cart to make the necessary adjustments. Much to our surprise, there on the road lay a small kitten. Until we picked it up, Daisy wasn't moving!

Daisy had two colts before we purchased her, and she never lost her maternal instincts. She loved colts, and every time she saw one, even on the other side of the road, she wanted it. Daisy would wander off in that direction until we directed her back to the road. Many times we saw young calves nursing Daisy, and she was in her glory! Believe it or not, she even tried to mother our Shetland pony, but he'd have none of it.

Winter was always an apprehensive time for Mom and Dad. Here were four young children in a cutter with a stove burning red-hot, travelling four and a half miles to school, often in weather that could be described as a true Saskatchewan blizzard. Dad always said he never worried about the horse doing her job and getting us home but was concerned about the harness snapping in extremely cold weather or the kids using poor judgement. If there was a blizzard and visibility was poor,

though, we would leave the reins loose. Daisy always brought us home.

Many gateposts were wiped out by us Christensen kids, for Daisy had one bad habit: I'm sure she dreamed of her cozy stall, for once we were in the cart (and we had to be quick!), she was off in a cloud of dust or snow, heedless of a minor obstruction such as a gatepost. This spirited pace was kept up only for about a quarter of a mile; then her after-school energy was burned off.

Daisy had tender feet and despised the gravelled portion of the road, so she chose to

JoAnn and Carl Christensen in a brand-new cutter equipped with a fire-holder and bells on the shafts. Perhaps even Daisy enjoyed the stylish rig as she took the children to Thistle Dale S.D. (Borden, Saskatchewan).

walk along the side of the road. It was funny and rather odd to see our travelled path on the main road, with the extra tire trail off to one side, the evidence of Daisy pampering her feet on the grassy area. To help her out a bit, Dad shoed her in the summer.

Winter was always an exciting time. It seemed by early November our Christmas concert parts were assigned, and there were new Christmas carols to learn. What better place to practise than on the way home from school? Many times we'd enjoy a treat during these special sojourns—leftover, frozen-solid sandwiches, which we thawed out and toasted on our cutter heater. M-m-m-m was that good! By the time the concert came along, I'm certain Daisy could have prompted us if we had forgotten our lines.

When the sun appeared and spring arrived, we'd slide open the front window and lean out, driving the horse and singing out at the top of our lungs. Our neighbours often teased us about the coyotes they heard howling that day!

We were appointed by the school district to haul drinking water to the school, which we did in a cream can. This, along with a sheaf of feed for Daisy's lunch, our lunch pails, school bags, and other necessities, filled our cart or cutter to the brim. Looking back through adult eyes, I wonder how on earth we packed it all in and still managed to find room to lark around in!

All our family members were proud of Daisy's ability as a racer. She was keenly competitive, and even though she had a cart or cutter behind her, she could outrun any of our friends' horses. Dad didn't like us racing Daisy, but since she enjoyed it every once in a while, we did!

After seeing us through grades one to ten, Daisy was retired to pasture. She spent her remaining years lovingly looked after on the farm, quietly passing away in her stall one winter's day at the age of twenty-seven years.

Many is the time we think of those days past, and now that the young children Daisy knew are around the middle-age stage, we often wish we could hitch up Daisy and go for a ride—just to take time to see the country, daydream, smell new-budding leaves and old harness, relive some good memories, and maybe have one last race! Ready, Daisy?

Dan Patch Was His Name

Norris Murray will never forget Dan Patch, named after the great race horse, whose blood coursed through his veins. Dan Patch travelled the two miles to school twice a day for twenty years and served all five of the Murray children faithfully.

Tony, hitched to the democrat, took the Hobson children to Cloverleaf S.D. (Chinook, Alberta) in 1928.

In later years, it was my duty to harness and hitch Dan Patch to the two-wheeled cart and leave him standing at the house gate. If for any reason we were not there at 8:30, he left for school on his own, with us walking a considerable distance behind. In the end, when we arrived at the school barn, Dan Patch would be standing patiently by, waiting to be unhitched and tied to the barn.

Often a race would develop on our way home from school, but Dan Patch only put up with so much of this. He grabbed the bit firmly in his teeth, ran through the ditch, then up onto the railroad track, and down the track at full gallop—with hats, scribblers, and dinner pails scattered along the way.

At the height of the drought years in our area, 1934, we had to ship out our cattle and horses; we kept only what we could feed. Dan Patch, of course, stayed, along with one team. The rest of the animals were shipped to eastern Manitoba to be wintered on government feed. The ration of straw and green Russian thistle that was fed to the animals left behind produced the most explosive diarrhoea. Our Dan Patch was no exception! It was necessary for us to erect a three-foot-high dashboard to protect us from that other indignity of the thirties. The horses we shipped away returned in the spring of '35. What an eyesore! They stumbled out of the boxcar and headed for home, Old Maud in the

143

lead. The animals were thin as rakes; the government feed must have gone somewhere else.

As the Depression deepened, the cart wheels were replaced with Model-T wheels and tires, which eventually ran on the rims when the tires wore out. One thing saved us: American dog trainers still came to our area every summer to train their bird dogs. They rented Dan Patch for fifteen dollars for the ladies to ride, as he could be trusted not to stumble or fall.

Dan Patch did not particularly like adults, but he responded with gentleness and caring to children. He would transport a three-year-old child on his back with infinite care to the neighbours but would run away from an adult when he realized there was work to be done. After school, when Dan Patch was hitched up to the cart to go home, the ten- and twelve-year-old boys would catch hold of his front and back legs on the same side and try to upset him. He would look around pathetically but would put up with the boys' capers without flinching.

As Dan Patch got older, his built-in time clock played tricks on him. One morning he was nowhere to be found, so we had to walk to school to find him. He had left for school very early in the morning—minus harness, cart, and children—and was in his stall in the school barn waiting to be tied up.

School days were over for most of us when Dan Patch lay down in the barn and stayed that way for four days. We had always been taught that once a horse was down for twenty-four hours, it would not be up again. The morning of the fifth day, when the stable doors were opened, he staggered to his feet. Thinking he wanted a drink, we let him outside; instead, off he went to school. He got half a mile from the house before dropping dead.

Only a few years later, Laddy, Paddy, Queenie, Maud, Jess, Trudy, and Morgan were gone, too, replaced by the rubber-tired tractor that didn't need to be fed at six o'clock in the morning and rested ten minutes of every hour.

Memories are made of this!

Credits

Index

Numbers in bold indicate pages where photographs appear.

146

About the Author

John C. Charyk, the author of *Syrup Pails and Gopher Tails*, a Canadian bestseller, and *The Biggest Day of the Year*, is also familiar to many as the author of the award-winning Little White Schoolhouse series.

Born in Glenbow, Alberta, Mr. Charyk taught in that province from 1928 to 1973, a record interrupted only by the Second World War, during which he served as a flying officer in England. In addition to holding Bachelor of Science, Bachelor of Education, and Master of Education degrees, Mr. Charyk is a life member of the Alberta Teachers' Federation, the highest honour that organization can bestow, was made a Fellow of the Canadian College of Teachers in 1971, and has received numerous awards for his achievements and contributions to education.

John Charyk has lived in Hanna, Alberta, since 1954. The high school there bears his name in recognition of his many years of service as its principal, and he was named Citizen of the Year in 1984. He maintains an active schedule as a historical researcher and lecturer, sharing his valuable collection of slides with schoolchildren and community groups.